INTRODUCTION TO THE
THEORY OF FINITE GROUPS

UNIVERSITY MATHEMATICAL TEXTS

GENERAL EDITORS

ALEXANDER C. AITKEN, D.Sc., F.R.S.
DANIEL E. RUTHERFORD, D.Sc., DR. MATH.

DETERMINANTS AND MATRICES . A. C. Aitken, D.Sc., F.R.S.
STATISTICAL MATHEMATICS . . A. C. Aitken, D.Sc., F.R.S.
THE THEORY OF ORDINARY DIFFERENTIAL EQUATIONS
J. C. Burkill, Sc.D., F.R.S.
WAVES . . . . . . C. A. Coulson, D.Sc., F.R.S.
ELECTRICITY . . . . . C. A. Coulson, D.Sc., F.R.S.
PROJECTIVE GEOMETRY . . . . T. E. Faulkner, Ph.D.
INTEGRATION . . . . . R. P. Gillespie, Ph.D.
PARTIAL DIFFERENTIATION . . . R. P. Gillespie, Ph.D.
INFINITE SERIES . . . . . J. M. Hyslop, D.Sc.
INTEGRATION OF ORDINARY DIFFERENTIAL EQUATIONS
E. L. Ince, D.Sc.

INTRODUCTION TO THE THEORY OF FINITE GROUPS
W. Ledermann, Ph.D., D.Sc.
GERMAN-ENGLISH MATHEMATICAL VOCABULARY
S. Macintyre, Ph.D. and E. Witte, M.A.
ANALYTICAL GEOMETRY OF THREE DIMENSIONS
W. H. McCrea, Ph.D., F.R.S.
TOPOLOGY . . . . . . E. M. Patterson, Ph.D.
FUNCTIONS OF A COMPLEX VARIABLE E. G. Phillips, M.A., M.Sc.
VOLUME AND INTEGRAL . W. W. Rogosinski, Dr. Phil., F.R.S.
VECTOR METHODS . . D. E. Rutherford, D.Sc., Dr. Math.
CLASSICAL MECHANICS . . D. E. Rutherford, D.Sc., Dr. Math.
SPECIAL FUNCTIONS OF MATHEMATICAL PHYSICS AND CHEMISTRY
I. N. Sneddon, D.Sc.
TENSOR CALCULUS . . . . . B. Spain, Ph.D.
THEORY OF EQUATIONS . . . . H. W. Turnbull, F.R.S.

INTRODUCTION TO THE
THEORY OF FINITE GROUPS

BY

WALTER LEDERMANN, Ph.D., D.Sc.
SENIOR LECTURER IN MATHEMATICS IN THE UNIVERSITY OF MANCHESTER

OLIVER AND BOYD
EDINBURGH AND LONDON
NEW YORK : INTERSCIENCE PUBLISHERS, INC.
1957

FIRST PUBLISHED 1949
SECOND REVISED EDITION 1953
THIRD REVISED EDITION 1957

PRINTED IN GREAT BRITAIN BY
R. AND R. CLARK, LTD., EDINBURGH
FOR OLIVER AND BOYD, LTD., EDINBURGH

FROM THE PREFACE OF THE FIRST EDITION

IT is hoped that this introduction to the Theory of Groups is sufficiently elementary to be understood by an Honours student in his second or third year.

Many will regret that the theory of matrix representation has not been included. In my opinion, however, this extensive subject should not be divorced from its context in the theory of linear associative algebras, and I felt that an adequate presentation of both of these disciplines was out of the question in the space at my disposal.

My warm thanks are due to the Editors for encouraging me to write this book, and especially to Dr. D. E. Rutherford for the great care and the helpful interest with which he has followed its progress from the day when the plan was first discussed during a holiday in the Highlands, until the last proof sheet was returned to the printers.

I am indebted to my colleague Mr. D. Rees for valuable suggestions and for checking the examples, and to my wife for helping with the proof reading and with the index.

Finally, I should like to express my appreciation of the efficiency with which the publishers have carried out their task under difficult conditions and of their never-failing courtesy.

W. LEDERMANN

MANCHESTER
May 1948

PREFACE TO THE SECOND EDITION

THE chapter on Abelian groups has been completely re-written in additive notation and now contains the Basis Theorem for finitely generated (infinite) Abelian groups. It is hoped that the inclusion of this topic will make the book more useful to students of topology, who can acquire a knowledge of the most essential facts of group theory by reading Chapters I, II, IV and VI, omitting the illustrations dealing with the symmetric group.

Changes have also been made in the presentation of the Isomorphism Theorems.

I am indebted to many friends and colleagues who have drawn my attention to misprints and errors in the first edition. I am particularly grateful to Mr. J. H. Williamson, who supplied a rather comprehensive list of misprints.

My thanks are due to Dr. P. J. Hilton for assisting in the proof reading and for making some valuable suggestions about the new material.

Finally, it is a pleasure to express my appreciation of the willingness with which the publishers have co-operated throughout the preparation of the new edition.

W. LEDERMANN

MANCHESTER
   June 1952

PREFACE TO THE THIRD EDITION

THE main new feature of this edition is the inclusion of a short chapter on generators and relations. This, it is hoped, will be valuable to students attending a course on algebraic topology ; and it will also serve as a first introduction to the theory of infinite groups, which has become so prominent in recent algebraical research.

W. LEDERMANN

MANCHESTER
   June 1956

CONTENTS

CONTENTS

CHAPTER IV

INVARIANT SUBGROUPS

CHAPTER V

SYLOW GROUPS AND PRIME POWER GROUPS

CHAPTER VI

ABELIAN GROUPS

CHAPTER I

THE GROUP CONCEPT

1. Introduction. The elementary operations of arithmetic consist in combining two numbers a and b in accordance with some well-defined rules so as to produce a unique third number c. For instance, if the **law of composition** is ordinary multiplication, we should have $c = ab$. When a and b are given, the number c can be found in each concrete case.

But we know that multiplication of two or more numbers obeys certain *formal laws* which hold for all products, irrespective of their numerical values, thus :

$$ab = ba \quad (commutative\ law) \qquad . \qquad . \quad (1.1)$$
$$(ab)c = a(bc) \quad (associative\ law) \qquad . \qquad . \quad (1.2)$$
$$1a = a1 = a. \quad . \qquad . \qquad . \qquad . \qquad . \quad (1.3)$$

The last equation serves to introduce one particular number called *unity*.

The second law states more explicitly that, if we put $ab = s$ and $bc = t$, then it is always true that $sc = at$.

In the axiomatic treatment of arithmetic it is customary to begin by laying down postulates or axioms such as (1.1), (1.2) and (1.3), and certain others dealing with addition as well as multiplication, and then to deduce the logical consequences of these postulates. It is immaterial, at the outset, whether the symbols a, b, . . . represent numbers as we normally understand them or other mathematical entities, or indeed whether they admit of any concrete interpretation at all. On the other hand, it will be conceded that it is the variety and depth of application in pure and applied mathematics which has caused one conceivable system of axioms to be preferred to another.

2. The Axioms of Group Theory. The abstract theory of groups deals with certain *sets of elements*

$$G = \{A, B, C, \ldots\}$$

with respect to which a *single law of composition* is defined. It is a matter of convention that the notation and nomenclature of *multiplication* are usually adopted to express the composition of abstract group elements. Thus we assume that any two elements A, B of G, equal or unequal, possess a unique *product* C, and we write

$$AB = C.$$

It is the most typical property of a group that this product C is itself one of its elements or, as it is often expressed, that a group is *closed with respect to multiplication*.

A complete system of axioms which a set G must obey, if it is to be a group, is given in the following:

DEFINITION 1. *A set G of a finite or infinite number of elements, for which a law of composition (" multiplication ") is defined, forms a group if the following conditions are satisfied :*

(I) **Closure :** *to every ordered * pair of elements* A, B *of G there belongs a unique element* C *of G, written*

$$C = AB,$$

which is called the product of A *and* B.

(II) **Associative law :** *if* A, B, C *are any three elements of G, which need not be distinct, then*

$$(AB)C = A(BC),$$

so that either side may be denoted by ABC.

* I.e. the pairs A, B and B, A are regarded as distinct if $A \neq B$.

(III) **Unit element :** G *contains an* * *element* I, *called the unit element or* **identity** *such that for every element* A *of* G

$$AI = IA = A.$$

(IV) **Inverse** *or* **reciprocal element :** *corresponding to every element* A *of* G, *there exists in* G *an* * *element* A^{-1} *such that*

$$AA^{-1} = A^{-1}A = I.$$

It will be observed that these postulates closely resemble those which govern ordinary multiplication, except that the *commutative law* is not required to hold for groups.

DEFINITION 2. *A group which has the additional property that for every two of its elements*

$$AB = BA$$

is called an **Abelian** † (*or* **commutative**) *group.*

The waiving of the commutative law for groups in general makes it necessary to distinguish between the elements AB and BA, which are sometimes called the right- and left-hand products of A by B.

It is quite possible that while the commutative law does not hold throughout the group, it may yet be valid for certain individual pairs of elements.

DEFINITION 3. *Two elements* A, B *are said to* **commute** (*or to be* **commutative,** *or* **permutable**) *if*

$$AB = BA.$$

It is worth while to dwell a little longer on the significance and immediate consequences of the group axioms stated in Definition 1, p. 2.

The *associative law* was enunciated only for three elements. But it implies more generally that a product of

---

* Its uniqueness will be proved later on, see pp. 5 and 6.
      † After N. H. Abel (1802–29).

B

n factors (in a given order) has a unique meaning, so that brackets may be inserted or omitted at will. Using axiom (II) as a basis of induction, we may assume that a product of fewer than n factors is already defined and that

$$A_1 A_2 \ldots A_r = (A_1 A_2 \ldots A_s)(A_{s+1} \ldots A_r),$$

where $1 < s < r < n$. It is required to show that

$$(A_1 \ldots A_r)(A_{r+1} \ldots A_n) = (A_1 \ldots A_s)(A_{s+1} \ldots A_n). \quad . \quad (1.4)$$

The left-hand side of (1.4) can be written

$$[(A_1 \ldots A_s)(A_{s+1} \ldots A_r)](A_{r+1} \ldots A_n) = [B_1 B_2]B_3,$$

say, where the products in round brackets are denoted by B_1, B_2, B_3 respectively. The right-hand side of (1.4) can be expressed as

$$(A_1 \ldots A_s)[(A_{s+1} \ldots A_r)(A_{r+1} \ldots A_n)] = B_1[B_2 B_3],$$

after the second factor has been broken up. By axiom (II)

$$[B_1 B_2]B_3 = B_1[B_2 B_3],$$

which proves the proposition (1.4). We are therefore entitled to omit the brackets altogether and denote either side of (1.4) by

$$A_1 A_2 \ldots A_n.$$

In particular, when all factors are identical we shall, as in ordinary algebra, write

$$AA \qquad\qquad = A^2,$$
$$(AA)A = A(AA) = A^3,$$
$$\ldots\ldots\ldots\ldots\ldots\ldots\ldots\ldots\ldots$$

Also, when n and m are positive integers,

$$A^m A^n = A^n A^m = A^{m+n} \quad . \quad\quad . \quad\quad . \quad (1.5)$$

and

$$(A^m)^n = A^{mn}. \quad . \quad\quad . \quad\quad . \quad\quad . \quad (1.6)$$

It is interesting to note that the familiar law of indices and the manipulation of powers of a *single* quantity finds its ultimate justification in the associative law of multiplication.

When A and B are distinct elements, we have in general

$$(AB)^n \neq A^n B^n \; ;$$

but when A and B commute,

$$(AB)^n = ABAB \ldots AB = A^n B^n \qquad . \qquad . \qquad (1.7)$$

and

$$A^m B^n = B^n A^m,$$

since we may rearrange the order of the factors as we please.

Multiplication by the **unit element** I, whether used as a right or a left factor, leaves every element of G unaltered. It follows that there can be only *one* such element. For supposing that J had the same properties as I, let us consider the product

$$IJ.$$

Since premultiplication by I leaves J unaltered, we have $IJ = J$; on the other hand, as postmultiplication by J has no effect on I, it follows that $IJ = I$; hence

$$J = IJ = I,$$

which proves the uniqueness of the unit element.

Also,

$$I = I^2 = I^3 = \ldots = I^n. \qquad . \qquad . \qquad (1.8)$$

The existence, within the group, of an *inverse* for every element A means that not only multiplication, but also left and right " division ", can be carried out within a group. Thus if A and B are any elements whatsoever, there exist elements X and Y such that

$$AX = B, \quad YA = B. \qquad . \qquad . \qquad (1.9)$$

In fact, we can express the solutions in the form

$$X = A^{-1}B, \quad Y = BA^{-1},$$

using the element A^{-1} referred to in postulate (IV) on p. 3. This argument also proves that the solutions of (1.9) are unique ; for if

$$AX_1 = AX_2 = B,$$

it would follow that

$$A^{-1}(AX_1) = A^{-1}(AX_2),$$

and therefore

$$X_1 = X_2.$$

Again, since A^{-1} itself is a solution of these equations when $B = I$, we infer that the inverse of any given element is unique.

It is important to note that A commutes with A^{-1}. Hence by (1.8) and (1.7)

$$I = I^n = (AA^{-1})^n = A^n (A^{-1})^n,$$

so that $(A^{-1})^n$ is the inverse of A^n ; it is customary to write

$$(A^n)^{-1} = (A^{-1})^n = A^{-n}. \qquad . \qquad . \qquad . \quad (1.10)$$

The reader will have no difficulty in convincing himself that the rules (1.5) and (1.6) are still valid when m or n are negative integers or zero, provided we put

$$A^0 = I. \qquad . \qquad . \qquad . \qquad . \quad (1.11)$$

In particular we observe that two powers of the same element always commute, thus

$$A^k A^l = A^l A^k. \qquad . \qquad . \qquad . \quad (1.12)$$

Since, for any two elements A and B,

$$(AB)(B^{-1}A^{-1}) = ABB^{-1}A^{-1} = I,$$

we have

$$(AB)^{-1} = B^{-1}A^{-1},$$

and more generally,

$$(AB \ldots K)^{-1} = K^{-1} \ldots B^{-1}A^{-1}. \qquad . \quad (1.13)$$

Lastly, we remark that I is the only **idempotent** element of the group, i.e. the only solution of the equation

$$X^2 = X. \qquad . \qquad . \qquad . \qquad . \qquad (1.14)$$

For on multiplying (1.14) by X^{-1} we obtain

$$X^{-1}X^2 = X^{-1}X,$$

i.e.
$$X = I.$$

3. Examples of Infinite Groups. The groups we are going to mention in this section contain an infinity of elements and are therefore called **infinite groups.**

(i) *All positive rational numbers form a group with respect to ordinary multiplication.* Indeed the product of two rational numbers is a rational number, the unit element is the rational number 1, and the inverse of every positive rational number is also such a number. This group is Abelian.

By way of contrast we might point out that the set of *positive integers* does *not* form a group with respect to multiplication, because the fourth postulate, the existence of an inverse, is not fulfilled.

(ii) *The set of all integers forms an Abelian group with respect to addition.* In this case it is customary to express the composition of elements by such an equation as

$$a + b = c.$$

The unit element is the number 0, because

$$a + 0 = 0 + a = a,$$

and the inverse of a is $-a$.

(iii) *Rotations about a fixed point* : if a rigid body is free to move about a fixed point O, every displacement of the body is equivalent to a rotation through an angle α about a line l passing through O. Such a displacement will be denoted by (l, α), or more briefly by a single letter A. If B is another displacement about the point O, the product

AB is defined as the displacement which results when A and B are carried out in succession (in this order *). This being the law of composition it is easy to verify the group postulates. The unit element is the " displacement " which, in fact, leaves the body in its original position, i.e. $I = (l, 0)$, where l is arbitrary. The inverse of (l, α) is $(l, -\alpha)$. We shall later (p. 87) prove the associative law for a certain general class of operations which includes the present type of displacement. The following illustration demonstrates that the commutative law is not always fulfilled : let 1234

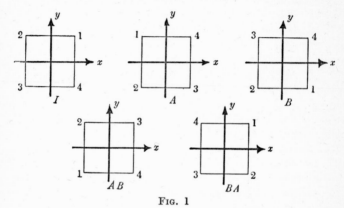

Fɪɢ. 1

denote a square lamina initially placed in the (x, y)-plane as indicated in fig. 1, the axis of z being at right angles to the plane of the lamina. We assume that $Oxyz$ is a right-handed system of reference, which is fixed in space. If, in the above notation,

$$A = \left(z, \frac{\pi}{2}\right), \quad B = (x, \pi),$$

it is easily verified that AB and BA give rise to different positions of the lamina so that $AB \neq BA$.

* Some authors take the reverse order.

(iv) *Groups of matrices* : the reader who is familiar with the elementary properties of matrices * will appreciate the excellent illustration of group theory afforded by matrix algebra and in particular by matrix multiplication. For the discussion of the associative law, the existence of the unit matrix and the reciprocal matrix, see *op. cit.* p. 12 and p. 53 respectively, or Chapter III, § 27 of the present book.

The following sets of matrices form groups with respect to matrix multiplication :

(a) *all non-singular matrices of a fixed order* n,
(b) *all orthogonal matrices of a fixed order* n,
(c) *all orthogonal matrices of a fixed order and of determinant* $+1$.

4. Alternative Axioms for Finite Groups. Groups which consist of a finite number of elements are of especial interest, and we shall henceforth be concerned only with **finite groups** unless the contrary is expressly stated. The number of elements in a finite group is called the **order** of the group.

In the case of finite groups the fundamental axioms (p. 2) may be replaced by the following alternative system of postulates which are sometimes easier to verify :

THEOREM 1. *A finite set of elements, for which a law of composition (" multiplication ") is defined, forms a group if*

(a) *the set is closed with respect to multiplication* ;
(b) *the associative law is satisfied* ;
(c) *right and left cancelling is permitted, i.e. each of the equations*
$$AX = BX \quad \text{and} \quad YA = YB$$

implies that $A = B$.

Proof. We shall show that condition (c) entails axioms (III) and (IV) on p. 3, i.e. we shall deduce from (c) the

* See A. C. Aitken, *Determinants and Matrices*, 9th edition.

existence of the unit and inverse elements.   Let

$$A_1, A_2, \ldots, A_g \qquad . \qquad . \qquad . \quad (1.15)$$

be the g distinct elements of the group G. If A is any one of them, the products

$$AA_1, AA_2, \ldots, AA_g \quad . \qquad . \qquad . \quad (1.16)$$

are elements of G in virtue of (a) and are distinct, because, by (c), an equation of the form $AA_i = AA_j$ implies that $A_i = A_j$. Thus the g elements written down in (1.16) are merely a different arrangement of those in (1.15). Therefore if X is any element of G whatsoever, there exists an element A_u such that

$$AA_u = X, \qquad . \qquad . \qquad . \qquad . \quad (1.17)$$

because X, which occurs in (1.15), must have a counterpart in (1.16).

Similarly, on postmultiplying the set (1.15) by A we conclude that there exists an element A_v such that

$$A_v A = X. \qquad . \qquad . \qquad . \qquad . \quad (1.18)$$

These conclusions apply in particular to the case when $A = X$, i.e. we infer that G contains two elements A_0 and $A_0{}'$ such that

$$AA_0 = A \qquad . \qquad . \qquad . \qquad . \quad (1.19)$$

and

$$A_0{}'A = A. \qquad . \qquad . \qquad . \qquad . \quad (1.20)$$

On premultiplying (1.17) by $A_0{}'$ we obtain $A_0{}'X = A_0{}'(AA_u) = (A_0{}'A)A_u = AA_u = X$,

i.e.
$$A_0{}'X = X. \qquad . \qquad . \qquad . \qquad . \quad (1.21)$$
Similarly,

$$XA_0 = X. \qquad . \qquad . \qquad . \qquad . \quad (1.22)$$

Thus we have shown that in equations (1.19) and (1.20) A may be replaced by X which, it will be remembered, was an arbitrary element of G, i.e. any element whatsoever remains unaltered when premultiplied by $A_0{}'$ or postmultiplied by A_0. In particular, on putting X equal to A_0 in (1.21) and X equal to A_0' in (1.22), we find that

$$A_0 = A_0'A_0 = A_0'.$$

This establishes the existence of a *unit element*, namely

$$I = A_0 = A_0' \; ;$$

its uniqueness follows at once by an application of (c) to the equation $AI = A$.

Let us now return to equations (1.17) and (1.18) and consider the case in which $X = I$. We conclude that G contains two elements A_r and A_r' such that

$$AA_r = I$$

and

$$A_r'A = I.$$

In order to prove that these two elements are equal we simplify the product $A_r'AA_r$ in two different ways by appealing to the associative law, namely

$$A_r'AA_r = (A_r'A)A_r = IA_r = A_r$$

and

$$A_r'AA_r = A_r'(AA_r) = A_r'I = A_r',$$

whence

$$A_r = A_r' = A^{-1},$$

say. The uniqueness of A^{-1} follows from the fact that, according to (c), there cannot be more than one solution of the equation

$$AX = I.$$

5. The Multiplication Table. In the abstract theory of groups when no reference is made to the nature of the elements, the group must be considered completely specified if all possible products AB are known or can be determined. For a finite group of order g there are g^2 such products, which may conveniently be listed in a $g \times g$ **multiplication table** as was suggested by A. Cayley.[*]

[*] *Phil. Mag.* vol. vii (**4**), 1854.

Example. We shall give a detailed discussion of a group of order 6 which may in many ways be regarded as typical. The elements will be denoted by

$$I, A, B, C, D, E, \qquad . \qquad . \qquad . \quad (1.23)$$

and the 36 products formed by them are set out in the following table :

	I	A	B	C	D	E
I	I	A	B	C	D	E
A	A	B	I	E	C	D
B	B	I	A	D	E	C
C	C	D	E	I	A	B
D	D	E	C	B	I	A
E	E	C	D	A	B	I

Table 1

For example, the product CD is that element which stands at the intersection of the row marked C and the column marked D; thus $CD = A$. Similarly, we find that $BA = I$, $EB = D$ and so on. Our task is to verify that the rules for composition summarized in Table 1 do in fact obey the group axioms laid down in Theorem 1 on p. 9 : the system (1.23) is obviously *closed* (postulate (a)) because the product of any two elements is again one of the six elements of the set. The *cancelling rule* (c) is also fulfilled ; for if U and V are distinct elements of the set, then $XU \neq XV$ whatever element X may be chosen ; this is seen at once from the table where the various elements XU occupy the row marked X, and inspection shows that the elements in each row are distinct. Similar remarks apply to the columns. Direct verification of the *associative law* (b) would be laborious as all equations of the form

$$(XY)Z = X(YZ) \qquad . \qquad . \qquad . \quad (1.24)$$

would have to be examined ; however, we shall later learn how this difficulty can often be overcome by indirect methods, and we shall then return to this example (p. 70). In the meantime the reader is recommended to check equation (1.24) at least in some particular cases, e.g.

$$(AC)D = ED = B,$$
$$A(CD) = AA = B.$$

Table 1 is not symmetrical with respect to the main diagonal, which illustrates the fact that in general $XY \neq YX$. But it will be observed that the element I always lies either on the diagonal or else occupies positions which are symmetrically placed in pairs about the diagonal. This illustrates the property that every element commutes with its inverse, e.g. $AB = BA = I$, showing that A and B are inverse elements of each other.

The rows and columns, including their headings, may be rearranged amongst themselves without affecting the information contained in the multiplication table. It is sometimes convenient to specify the rows not by the elements themselves but by their inverses; thus Table 1 is equivalent to

	I	A	B	C	D	E
I	I	A	B	C	D	E
A^{-1}	B	I	A	D	E	C
B^{-1}	A	B	I	E	C	D
C^{-1}	C	D	E	I	A	B
D^{-1}	D	E	C	B	I	A
E^{-1}	E	C	D	A	B	I

Table 2

In a multiplication table of this type the unit element naturally occupies all the positions of the main diagonal.

Postulate (c) on p. 9 is equivalent to the demand that no element be repeated in any one row or column of the $g \times g$ multiplication table, i.e. all g elements appear in some order in each row or column. Such an arrangement is commonly called a *latin square*. But it is not true that conversely every latin square can be interpreted as the multiplication table of a finite group; for while the condition of closure and cancelling would indeed be fulfilled, the associative law might not be satisfied. This is shown by the following example $(g = 5)$. In the latin square

	I	A	B	C	D
I	I	A	B	C	D
A	A	I	D	B	C
B	B	C	I	D	A
C	C	D	A	I	B
D	D	B	C	A	I

Table 3

the break-down of the associative law is exemplified by the equations

$$(AB)C = DC = A,$$
$$A(BC) = AD = C.$$

Thus Table 3 cannot be regarded as the multiplication table of a group.

6. Examples of Finite Groups.

(i) *The numbers* 1, i, − 1, − i *form an Abelian group of order* 4 *with respect to ordinary multiplication* $(i = \sqrt{-1})$. The reader is recommended to construct the 4×4 multiplication table.

(ii) Consider the six functions

$$f_1(z) = z, \quad f_2(z) = \frac{1}{1-z}, \quad f_3(z) = \frac{z-1}{z},$$

$$f_4(z) = \frac{1}{z}, \quad f_5(z) = 1 - z, \quad f_6(z) = \frac{z}{z-1},$$

which are the values of the cross-ratio of four points when these points are permuted in all possible ways, and let the law of composition be defined as *substitution of one function in another*; e.g.

$$f_4 f_3 = f_4\{f_3(z)\} = \frac{1}{f_3(z)} = \frac{z}{z-1} = f_6,$$

and so on. It will be found that these functions form a *closed* set, the part of the *unit element* being played by $f_1(z)$. The multiplication table is readily constructed thus :

	f_1	f_2	f_3	f_4	f_5	f_6
f_1	f_1	f_2	f_3	f_4	f_5	f_6
f_2	f_2	f_3	f_1	f_6	f_4	f_5
f_3	f_3	f_1	f_2	f_5	f_6	f_4
f_4	f_4	f_5	f_6	f_1	f_2	f_3
f_5	f_5	f_6	f_4	f_3	f_1	f_2
f_6	f_6	f_4	f_5	f_2	f_3	f_1

Table 4

The *associative law* can be verified or established by indirect arguments (Chap. III, § 27).

(iii) *Classes of residues.* Every positive integer (>1) gives rise to a certain finite Abelian group in the following way : let m be a fixed positive integer (>1), which will henceforth be referred to as the **modulus**. *Two integers* x *and* y *are said to be* **congruent** *to each other with regard to the modulus* m *if* m *is a factor of* x−y ; *we write symbolically*

$$x \equiv y \ (\text{mod. } m).$$

Thus two integers are congruent with respect to m if and only if they differ by an exact (positive or negative) multiple of m ; e.g. $3 \equiv 18$ (mod. 5), $-2 \equiv 14$ (mod. 8), $12 \equiv 0$ (mod. 3).

It follows that any integer whatsoever is congruent, with regard to the modulus m, to one and only one of the numbers

$$0, 1, 2, \ldots, m-2, m-1, \qquad . \qquad . \quad (1.25)$$

which are therefore said to form a **complete set of residues** relative to m ; they are in fact the least non-negative residues relative to m.

Bearing in mind that the congruence relation

$$x \equiv y \ (\text{mod. } m)$$

is equivalent to an equation of the form

$$x = y + km$$

where k is a certain integer, it is easy to verify the following rules : *if* $x_1 \equiv y_1$ (mod. m) *and* $x_2 \equiv y_2$ (mod. m), *then*

(A) $$c_1 x_1 + c_2 x_2 \equiv c_1 y_1 + c_2 y_2 \ (\text{mod. } m),$$

where c_1 *and* c_2 *are any integers, and*

(M) $$x_1 x_2 \equiv y_1 y_2 \ (\text{mod. } m).$$

These rules show a remarkable resemblance to those for ordinary equations. Yet the following important difference should be carefully noted : while the equation $kx = ky$ implies that $x = y$ provided $k \neq 0$, we can only state that

(D) $$kx \equiv ky \ (\text{mod. } m) \qquad . \quad . \quad . \ (1.26)$$
implies that

$$x \equiv y \ (\text{mod. } m),$$

*provided** that* $(m, k) = 1$. Indeed (1.26) is equivalent to the statement†

$$m \mid k(x - y),$$

and if m is prime to k, it follows that

$$m \mid x - y,$$
i.e. $$x \equiv y \ (\text{mod. } m).$$

The number of integers in the set $0, 1, \ldots, m - 1$ *which are prime to* m *is denoted by* $\phi(m)$ (**Euler's function**). Thus, $\phi(9)$ denotes the number of integers between 0 and 8 (in-

---

* We use the symbol (a, b) to denote the highest common factor of a and b; in particular $(m, k) = 1$ means that m and k are (relatively) prime.

† The symbol $a \mid b$ expresses that a is a factor of b, i.e. that there exists an integer q such that $b = aq$. We shall use the fact that if $a \mid bc$ and $(a, c) = 1$, then $a \mid b$.

clusive) which are prime to 9 ; there are six such integers, namely 1, 2, 4, 5, 7, 8, so that $\phi(9) = 6$.

If p is a prime number, all but the first of the integers $0, 1, 2, \ldots, p-1$ are prime to p, whence

$$\phi(p) = p - 1. \quad . \quad . \quad . \quad (1.27)$$

Again, if $m = p^r$, only the multiples of p in the set $0, 1, 2, \ldots, p^r - 1$ are not prime to p^r ; as there are evidently p^{r-1} such multiples, namely hp where $h = 0, 1, 2, \ldots, p^{r-1} - 1$, it follows that

$$\phi(p^r) = p^r - p^{r-1}. \quad . \quad . \quad (1.28)$$

It is customary to put

$$\phi(1) = 1. \quad . \quad . \quad . \quad (1.29)$$

Those of the numbers (1.25) which are prime to m form a sub-set **M** which we shall denote by

$$\mathbf{M} : a_1, a_2, \ldots, a_{\phi(m)}, \quad . \quad . \quad (1.30)$$

where $0 < a_i < m$. One of these numbers, say a_1, is equal to 1. The product of any two is a number which is certainly prime to m though it may be greater than m and therefore not included in (1.30) ; but it is in any case *congruent* to one of these residues, as is indeed any integer which is prime to m. Thus we may write

$$a_i a_k \equiv a_l \text{ (mod. } m) \quad . \quad . \quad (1.31)$$

and define a law of composition for residues as *ordinary multiplication followed* (if necessary) *by reduction to the least positive residue with regard to* m ; e.g.

$$4 \times 5 \equiv 2 \text{ (mod. 9)}, \quad 2 \times 7 \equiv 5 \text{ (mod. 9)} \textit{ etc.}$$

It is clear that this law of composition, being derived from ordinary multiplication, is both *commutative* and *associative*. Again, as we are concerned only with residues prime to m, Rule (D) (p. 16) may be applied, i.e. if a, b and x are any members of **M**, then

$$ax \equiv bx \text{ (mod. } m) \textit{ implies that } a \equiv b \text{ (mod. } m).$$

This establishes the *cancelling rule* (c) of Theorem 1, p. 9. Thus we can summarize our results in the

THEOREM 2. *The least positive residues prime to* m *form an Abelian group* M *of order* $\phi(m)$ *if the law of composition is defined as multiplication followed by reduction relative to the modulus* m.

The unit element of M is obviously equal to 1, which always occurs in the set (1.30). Also since M is a group, every element a of M possesses a unique inverse a' such that

$$aa' \equiv 1 \ (\text{mod. } m),$$

or expressed as an ordinary equation

$$aa' = 1 + xm, \qquad . \qquad . \qquad . \qquad (1.32)$$

where x is a certain integer. If b is any number prime to m, it is of the form

$$b = a + ym, \qquad . \qquad . \qquad . \qquad (1.33)$$

where a is a suitable element of M. On multiplying (1.33) by a' and substituting for aa' from (1.32) we get

$$a'b - (a'y + x)m = 1.$$

This is a well-known result,* namely that *if* b *and* m *are relatively prime, then integers* u *and* v *exist such that*

$$ub + vm = 1 ; \qquad . \qquad . \qquad . \qquad (1.34)$$

in our notation $u = a'$ and $v = -(a'y + x)$.

7. Isomorphic Groups. On closer scrutiny it will be observed that Table 1 (p. 12) differs from Table 4 (p. 15) merely in respect of notation, so that from an abstract point of view they are regarded as representing the same group. In fact, if we establish the (1, 1)-correspondence

---

* The argument in the text is not offered as a proof of (1.34), which is usually obtained by means of Euclid's algorithm, and in its turn forms the basis of rule D.

$$f_1 \longleftrightarrow I, \quad f_2 \longleftrightarrow A, \quad f_3 \longleftrightarrow B,$$
$$f_4 \longleftrightarrow C, \quad f_5 \longleftrightarrow D, \quad f_6 \longleftrightarrow E \quad . \quad . \; (1.35)$$

the identity of the tables becomes evident ; i.e. any relation derived from Table 4 is in virtue of the correspondence (1.35) carried over into a correct relation between the elements of Table 1, and vice versa; e.g.

$$f_4 f_3 = f_6 \quad \text{becomes} \quad CB = E.$$

This is an illustration of a concept which is of fundamental importance in the theory of groups.

DEFINITION 4. *Two groups* $G = \{A, \; B, \ldots\}$ *and* $G' = \{A', \; B', \ldots\}$ *are said to be* **isomorphic** * *if a* (1, 1)-*correspondence*

$$A \longleftrightarrow A', \quad B \longleftrightarrow B', \ldots$$

can be established between their elements such that

$$AB = C \quad \text{implies} \quad A'B' = C',$$

and vice versa, or more briefly if

$$(AB)' = A'B'.$$

Paraphrasing this definition, we may say that *isomorphic groups have the same* **structure** *although they may differ in respect of the notation and nature of their elements.*

Example 1. The following groups of order 4 are isomorphic, the law of composition for each being stated in brackets :

(α) *the numbers*   1, i, -1, $-i$,   (*ordinary multiplication*)

(β) *the matrices*   (*matrix multiplication*)

$$\begin{bmatrix} 1 & 0 \\ 0 & 1 \end{bmatrix}, \quad \begin{bmatrix} 0 & 1 \\ -1 & 0 \end{bmatrix}, \quad \begin{bmatrix} -1 & 0 \\ 0 & -1 \end{bmatrix}, \quad \begin{bmatrix} 0 & -1 \\ 1 & 0 \end{bmatrix}$$

(γ) *the residues*   1, 2, 4, 3 (mod. 5)   (*multiplication and reduction* mod. 5)

---

* Some authors use the expression " *simply isomorphic* " in this connection, see footnote on p. 106.

C

Indeed if the elements of each set are renamed I, A, B, C (in this order), their common multiplication table is seen to be

	I	A	B	C
I	I	A	B	C
A	A	B	C	I
B	B	C	I	A
C	C	I	A	B

Table 5

E.g. the abstract equation

$$CB = A$$

is interpreted

in (α) as $(-i)(-1) = i$,

in (β) as $\begin{bmatrix} 0 & -1 \\ 1 & 0 \end{bmatrix} \begin{bmatrix} -1 & 0 \\ 0 & -1 \end{bmatrix} = \begin{bmatrix} 0 & 1 \\ -1 & 0 \end{bmatrix}$,

in (γ) as $3 \times 4 \equiv 2$ (mod. 5).

In a similar manner all other properties of the abstract Table 5 are reflected in the concrete groups (α), (β) and (γ).

Example 2.   Consider the following groups of order 4 where in each case the law of composition is stated in brackets :

(a) *the functions* z, $-z$, $\dfrac{1}{z}$, $-\dfrac{1}{z}$ (*substitution*, see p. 14)

(b) *the matrices*   (*matrix multiplication*)

$\begin{bmatrix} 1 & 0 \\ 0 & 1 \end{bmatrix}$, $\begin{bmatrix} 1 & 0 \\ 0 & -1 \end{bmatrix}$, $\begin{bmatrix} -1 & 0 \\ 0 & 1 \end{bmatrix}$, $\begin{bmatrix} -1 & 0 \\ 0 & -1 \end{bmatrix}$

(c) *the residues* $1, 3, 5, 7$ (mod. 8)   (*multiplication and reduction* mod. 8)

If the elements of each set are denoted by I, A, B, C, it will be seen that they have the same multiplication table, namely

	I	A	B	C
I	I	A	B	C
A	A	I	C	B
B	B	C	I	A
C	C	B	A	I

Table 6

It is left to the reader to verify this statement. We would point out, however, that the groups represented by Tables 5 and 6 respectively are certainly *not* isomorphic ; in the latter the square of each element is equal to I, which is evidently not the case in Table 5. Incidentally, we have learned that groups of the same order may well be of different structure.

8. The Order (Period) of an Element. Let A be an element of a group G of order g and consider the set of powers of A,

$$I, A, A^2, A^3, \ldots, \qquad . \quad . \quad . \quad (1.36)$$

all of which are of course elements of G. Since G is a finite group, these elements cannot all be distinct, i.e. we must have a relation

$$A^k = A^l,$$

where $k > l$, say. Hence

$$A^{k-l} = I,$$

which shows that in a finite group some power of every element is equal to the unit element.

DEFINITION 5. *The least positive integer* h *for which* A^h *is equal to the unit element is called the* **order** (*or* **period**) *of* A.

Thus if A is of order h, then

$$A^h = I,$$

but

$$A^x \neq I,$$

when $0 < x < h$.

Again, if m is a multiple of h, say

$$m = hq,$$

we have

$$A^m = (A^h)^q = I^q = I.$$

The converse of this proposition is also true; in fact, we shall prove

THEOREM 3.   *If* A *is of order* h, *then* $A^m = I$ *if, and only if,* m *is a multiple of* h.

Proof.   Divide m by h and let q be the quotient and r the remainder, thus

$$m = hq + r,$$

where

$$0 \leqslant r < h. \quad . \quad . \quad . \quad . \quad (1.37)$$

Hence

$$I = A^m = A^{hq+r} = A^{hq}A^r = I^q A^r = A^r.$$

Since h is the order of A, this equation is impossible unless $r = 0$; i.e. m must be a multiple of h.

The following facts about the order of an element are frequently used:

(i) *The unit element* I *is the only element of order one.*

(ii) *The elements* A *and* A^{-1} *are always of the same order* (see (iv)).

(iii) *If* $B = P^{-1}AP$ *where* P *is any element whatsoever, then* A *and* B *are of the same order.*   For

$$B^2 = (P^{-1}AP)(P^{-1}AP) = P^{-1}AIAP = P^{-1}A^2P,$$

and generally,

$$B^k = P^{-1}A^kP, \quad A^k = PB^kP^{-1};$$

thus if $A^k = I$, we have $B^k = P^{-1}IP = I$, and vice versa.

(iv) *The order of any power of* A *cannot exceed the order of* A.   For if $A^h = I$ and $B = A^s$, then $B^h = A^{sh} = (A^h)^s = I^s = I$. Moreover, *if* A *is of order* h *and if* s *is prime to* h, *then* A^s *and* A *are of the same order.*   As $(s, h) = 1$, we can find two integers u and v (see p. 18) such that $us + vh = 1$.   Hence if $B = A^s$, we have

$$B^u = A^{us} = A^{1-vh} = AA^{-vh} = AI = A.$$

Therefore, A is a power of B which is itself a power of A, whence A and B are of the same order.

The following theorem allows us to resolve a given element of composite order into factors of simpler orders:

THEOREM 4. *If* C *is of order* mn *where* m *and* n *are relatively prime, then* C *can be expressed in one, and only one, way as the product of two commutative elements* M *and* N *of orders* m *and* n *respectively.*

Proof. 1. Let $A = C^n$ and $B = C^m$; the elements A and B commute because they are powers of the same element C. We have

$$A^m = C^{nm} = I, \quad B^n = C^{mn} = I,$$

whence we infer that m and n are the orders of A and B respectively; for if a smaller (positive) power of A or B were equal to unit the element, we should get a contradiction to the fact that C was of order mn.

Since m and n are relatively prime, we can find integers u and v (see (1.34)) such that

$$un + vm = 1. \quad . \quad . \quad . \quad (1.38)$$

Hence

$$C = C^{un+vm} = (C^n)^u (C^m)^v = A^u B^v.$$

We deduce from (1.38) that u is prime to m; for if any factor (>1) were common to u and m, it would divide each term on the left-hand side of (1.38) and therefore also the right-hand side, which is absurd Hence by proposition (iv), p. 22, A^u is of order m. Similarly, B^v is of order n. Also, since A and B commute, so do A^u and B^v. Thus if we put

$$M = A^u, \quad N = B^v$$

we have

$$C = MN, \quad . \quad . \quad . \quad (1.39)$$

where M and N fulfil all the conditions of the theorem.

2. In order to prove the uniqueness of the decomposition (1.39) suppose that

$$C = MN = M_1 N_1, \quad . \quad . \quad . \quad (1.40)$$

where M commutes with N, and M_1 with N_1, and where the orders of M and M_1 are m, and those of N and N_1 are n. Raising (1.40) to the $(nu)^{th}$ power, we get

$$M^{nu}N^{nu} = M_1{}^{nu}N_1{}^{nu},$$
$$M^{nu} = M_1{}^{nu},$$

whence by using (1.38)

$$M^{1-mv} = M_1{}^{1-mv},$$
$$M(M^m)^{-v} = M_1(M_1{}^m)^{-v},$$
$$MI^{-v} = M_1 I^{-v},$$

i.e.

$$M = M_1.$$

Equation (1.40) now at once shows that, likewise,

$$N = N_1.$$

9. Cyclic Groups.

Definition 6. *A group whose elements can all be expressed as powers of a single element is called a* **cyclic** *group.*

The general form of a cyclic group of order c is

$$C : I, A, A^2, \ldots, A^{c-1}, \qquad . \qquad (1.41)$$

where c is the least positive integer such that

$$A^c = I.$$

We say that C is **generated** by A.

The order of a cyclic group is equal to that of its generating element; conversely, *if a group of order* c *contains an element of order* c, *then the group is cyclic.* The generating element is not uniquely determined; indeed if e is any integer prime to c and $0 < e < c$, then A^e may be taken as the generating element of the group (1.41) (see (iv) p. 22).

All cyclic groups of the same order are isomorphic, as

may be seen by making their generating elements correspond to one another; *there is, in fact, one, and only one (abstract), cyclic group for any given order.*

All cyclic groups are Abelian.

Example 1. If $\gamma = e^{2\pi i/c}$ (a primitive c^{th} root of unity), then the numbers

$$1, \gamma, \gamma^2, \ldots, \gamma^{c-1}$$

form a cyclic group of order c with respect to multiplication, because c is the least positive exponent such that $\gamma^c = 1$.

Example 2. The residues

$$0, 1, 2, \ldots, m-1$$

with respect to the modulus m form a cyclic group of order m, if the law of composition is addition followed by reduction to the least non-negative residue relative to m; e.g., if $m > 4$

$$(m-2) + 4 = m + 2 \equiv 2,$$
$$(m-3) + 3 = m \quad\quad \equiv 0.$$

The operations $I, A, A^2, \ldots, A^{c-1}$ of a cyclic group may be interpreted geometrically as rotations in a plane about a fixed point O. The group is generated by the rotation through an angle $2\pi/c$; any point on which this operation is carried out c times in succession returns to its original position after describing a complete circle (hence the name " cyclic " group).

Examples

(1) Prove that the following sets of numbers form infinite (Abelian) groups with respect to ordinary multiplication :

    (a) $\{2^k\}$ $(k = 0, \pm 1, \pm 2, \ldots)$.

    (b) $\left\{ \dfrac{1+2m}{1+2n} \right\}$ $(m, n = 0, \pm 1, \pm 2, \ldots)$.

    (c) $\{\cos \theta + i \sin \theta\}$, where θ runs over all rational numbers.

(2) Why do the positive rational numbers not form a group when the law of composition for a and b is defined as a/b ?

(3) If A is the operation which replaces x by $\alpha x + \beta$, prove

that A is of finite order if, and only if, α is a root of unity other than 1.

In examples (4) to (8) the associative law is assumed to hold for all elements involved.

(4) If A, B and AB are of order 2, prove that A and B commute.

(5) Prove that the elements AB and BA have the same order.

(6) If $BA = A^mB^n$, prove that the elements A^mB^{n-2}, $A^{m-2}B^n$ and AB^{-1} have the same order.

(7) If $B^{-1}AB = A^k$, prove that $B^{-r}A^sB^r = A^{sk^r}$.

(8) If $AB = BA^k$, show that $A^uB^v = B^vA^{uk^v}$ and $(B^vA^u)^t = B^{tv}A^w$, where $w = u(k^{tv} - 1)/(k^v - 1)$.

(9) Prove that a group is Abelian if, and only if, the correspondence $A \longleftrightarrow A^{-1}$, $B \longleftrightarrow B^{-1}$, ... represents an isomorphism.

(10) Show that a group of even order contains an odd number of elements of order 2.

(11) Show that the matrices

$$\begin{bmatrix} 1 & 0 \\ 0 & 1 \end{bmatrix}, \begin{bmatrix} \omega & 0 \\ 0 & \omega^2 \end{bmatrix}, \begin{bmatrix} \omega^2 & 0 \\ 0 & \omega \end{bmatrix}, \begin{bmatrix} 0 & 1 \\ 1 & 0 \end{bmatrix}, \begin{bmatrix} 0 & \omega^2 \\ \omega & 0 \end{bmatrix}, \begin{bmatrix} 0 & \omega \\ \omega^2 & 0 \end{bmatrix},$$

where $\omega^3 = 1$, $\omega \neq 1$, form a group of order 6 with respect to matrix multiplication. Prove that this group is isomorphic with that discussed on p. 12.

(12) Show that the identical operation and the rotations through π about any one of three mutually perpendicular intersecting lines form a group of order 4. Construct its multiplication table.

(13) Find the order of each element in the multiplicative group of residues 1, 2, 3, 4, 5, 6 prime to 7. Show that the group is cyclic of order 6, and that it can be generated by 3 or 5, but not by any of the other elements.

Write 5 as a product of two residues of orders 2 and 3 respectively.

(14) Prove that if a finite set of matrices forms a group, the latent roots of each matrix are roots of unity.

(15) Show that the set of all matrices

$$A(v) = \left(1 - \frac{v^2}{c^2}\right)^{-\frac{1}{2}} \begin{bmatrix} 1 & -v \\ \dfrac{-v}{c^2} & 1 \end{bmatrix},$$

where v varies in the interval $-c < v < c$, c being a positive constant, form a " continuous " group in the sense that

$$A(v_1)A(v_2) = A(v_3),$$

where
$$v_3 = \frac{v_1 + v_2}{1 + \dfrac{v_1 v_2}{c^2}}. \qquad \textbf{(Lorentz Group)}$$

ANSWERS.   12. Table 6, p. 21.   13. $5 \equiv 6.2$ (mod. 7).

CHAPTER II

COMPLEXES AND SUBGROUPS

10. The Calculus of Complexes. In this chapter we shall discuss some general properties of abstract (finite) groups. We imagine that a certain group

$$G : A_1, A_2, \ldots, A_g \quad . \quad . \quad . \quad (2.1)$$

of order g is given and that all elements with which we are concerned belong to this group. In particular it will be assumed that the *associative law* and the *cancelling rule* (p. 9) have been established once for all.

We shall find it convenient to examine subsets or **complexes** of elements of G. In order to express that a complex K consists of the elements $A, B, C, \ldots$ we use the notation

$$K = A + B + C + \ldots \quad . \quad . \quad . \quad (2.2)$$

We would emphasize that this symbol K does not represent an element of G, but a collection of such elements. The only law of composition for group elements continues to be denoted by the conventional formalism of multiplication, and no element can be regarded as the sum of two elements; to put it more briefly, the " + " signs in (2.2) stand for the word " and ", and not for " plus ".*

A complex is considered completely given if the *distinct* elements occurring in it are known, no account being taken of their order or of duplicates among them; thus

$$A + B + A + C + B + A = A + B + C = B + A + C = \ldots.$$

We shall learn to manipulate complexes as if they were independent entities, though different in nature from group

---

* No distinction will be made between a particular element and the complex consisting of this one element.

elements, and we shall establish two laws of composition for complexes, namely, *addition* and *multiplication*.

The **sum** of two complexes K and L is the complex which consists of all elements of K and L combined. Thus if

$$K = K_1 + K_2 + \ldots + K_k \quad \text{and} \quad L = L_1 + L_2 + \ldots + L_l, \quad (2.3)$$

$$K + L = K_1 + \ldots + K_k + L_1 + \ldots + L_l. \quad . \quad (2.4)$$

E.g., if $K = A + B + C$ and $L = A + B + D$ we have

$$K + L = A + B + C + D.$$

Addition of complexes is obviously *commutative* and *associative*, i.e.

$$K + L = L + K, \quad (K + L) + M = K + (L + M).$$

Note that

$$K + K = K, \quad . \quad . \quad . \quad (2.5)$$

since duplicates of elements are ignored.

The **product** of two complexes is the complex obtained by formal expansion, thus

$$KL = (K_1 + K_2 + \ldots + K_k)(L_1 + L_2 + \ldots + L_l)$$
$$= K_1 L_1 + K_1 L_2 + \ldots + K_k L_l. \quad . \quad (2.6)$$

E.g., in the group represented by Table 1, p. 12, we have

$$(I + A + D)(B + D) = B + D + AB + AD + DB + D^2$$
$$= B + D + I + C + C + I = I + B + C + D.$$

If one of the complexes consists of a single element P, we get

$$KP = (K_1 + \ldots + K_k)P = K_1 P + \ldots + K_k P$$

and

$$PK = P(K_1 + \ldots + K_k) = PK_1 + \ldots + PK_k.$$

Multiplication of complexes is in general non-commutative, but it is *associative* and *distributive*, thus

$$K(LM) = (KL)M, \qquad . \qquad . \qquad . \qquad (2.7)$$
$$K(L+M) = KL + KM, \qquad . \qquad . \qquad . \qquad (2.8)$$
$$(K+L)M = KM + LM. \qquad . \qquad . \qquad . \qquad (2.9)$$

These properties follow at once from the definitions.

If each element of K is an element of L, we say K is *contained* in L, and we write

$$K \subset L \quad \text{or} \quad L \supset K;$$

this includes the case in which K and L are in fact identical. Evidently, the two relations

$$K \subset L \quad \text{and} \quad K \supset L$$

hold simultaneously if, and only if,

$$K = L.$$

It is, in general, not permissible to apply the cancelling rule to complexes, i.e. from the equation

$$KL = KM$$

it does *not* follow that

$$L = M. \qquad . \qquad . \qquad . \qquad (2.10)$$

However, if one factor is a single element P, we can infer (2.10) whenever

$$PL = PM \quad \text{or} \quad LP = MP . \qquad . \qquad . \qquad (2.11)$$

holds, because (2.11) may be multiplied by P^{-1} on the left or on the right, yielding (2.10) on account of (2.7).

Note that *if* $L \subset K$, *then* $PL \subset PK$ *and* $LQ \subset KQ$ *where* P *and* Q *are any elements whatever.*

When, in exceptional cases, two complexes do *commute* we have

$$KL = LK. \qquad . \qquad . \qquad . \qquad (2.12)$$

This does *not* mean that every element of K commutes with every element of L; all that is implied by (2.12) is that every element of KL is some element of LK, and vice versa, i.e. that every product of the form $K_\alpha L_\beta$ can also be written in the form $L_\rho K_\sigma$ and that every element of the form $L_\gamma K_\delta$ is equal to an element $K_\lambda L_\mu$. In particular, if a complex K commutes with a single element P we have

$$KP = PK,$$

which may also be written

$$P^{-1}KP = K.$$

Such cases will be of great importance later (Chapter IV).

11. Subgroups. We are particularly interested in those complexes of G whose elements obey the group postulates ; such complexes are called **subgroups** of G. Every group G has two trivial or **improper subgroups**, namely, G itself and the group which consists of the unit element by itself $(I^2 = I)$; all other subgroups are called **proper subgroups**. In order that

$$H = (H_1, H_2, \ldots, H_h)$$

be a subgroup of G, its elements must satisfy the fundamental group postulates contained in the definition on p. 2 or, in the case of finite groups, the equivalent requirements laid down in the theorem on p. 9. Since the associative law and the cancelling rule hold for all elements of G, including those of H, it remains only to consider the postulate of closure. Thus we have

THEOREM 1. *A non-empty complex H of a finite group G is a subgroup if, and only if, it is closed with respect to multiplication.*

We note that the property of closure *implies* that the unit element of G belongs to H, and that the inverse of every element of H also lies in H.

In the example on p. 12 the complex $H = I + A + B$ is a subgroup of order 3 ; for its closure is made evident by the multiplication table (Table 1) where the nine places, in which the rows and columns headed I, A, B intersect, are occupied solely by the elements I, A, B.

In the calculus of complexes Theorem 1 takes the more concise form :

CRITERION 1. *A non-empty complex H of a finite group G is a subgroup if, and only if,*

$$H^2 \subset H. \qquad . \qquad . \qquad . \qquad (2.13)$$

Proof. (i) The relation (2.13) means that the product of any two elements of H is contained in H, i.e. that H is closed ; hence if (2.13) is fulfilled, H is a subgroup. (ii) Conversely, if H is a subgroup, it is closed and therefore (2.13) is true.

It will presently be shown that (2.13) may be replaced by a more precise statement ; but we shall first establish the following :

LEMMA 1. *If H is a group and if* H *is any one of its elements, then*

$$HH = H = HH. \qquad . \qquad . \qquad . \qquad (2.14)$$

Proof. Since H is closed we have

$$HH \subset H, \qquad . \qquad . \qquad . \qquad (2.15)$$

where H is any element of H. On the other hand, the complexes

$$H = H_1 + H_2 + \ldots + H_h \quad \text{and} \quad HH = H_1H + H_2H + \ldots + H_hH$$

contain the same number of elements, because we infer from the cancelling rule that $H_iH \neq H_jH$ unless $H_i = H_j$. Hence we may modify (2.15) and state that $HH = H$. Similarly, we can show that $HH = H$.

COROLLARY. *If H is a group and if C is a complex contained in H, then*

$$HC = H = CH. \qquad . \qquad . \qquad . \qquad (2.16)$$

For let $C = H' + H'' + \ldots$; then by the lemma

$$HC = HH' + HH'' + \ldots = H + H + \ldots = H$$

on discarding duplicates (see (2.5)).

On applying this result to the case in which $C = H$ we see that, *if H is a group*, $H^2 = H$. Conversely, if this equation is satisfied, we have *a fortiori* $H^2 \subset H$ whence we deduce from Criterion 1 (p. 32) that H is in fact a group. Thus we have established

CRITERION 2. *A non-empty complex H of a finite group G is a subgroup if, and only if,*

$$H^2 = H. \qquad . \qquad . \qquad . \qquad (2.17)$$

From a given subgroup it is often possible to derive further subgroups by means of the following theorem:

THEOREM 2. *If H is a subgroup and if P is any element of G, then the complex*

$$H' = P^{-1}HP$$

is a subgroup isomorphic with H, though not necessarily distinct from it.

Proof. Using Criterion 2 we have by hypothesis $H^2 = H$. Hence

$$(H')^2 = (P^{-1}HP)(P^{-1}HP) = P^{-1}H^2P = P^{-1}HP = H',$$

i.e. H' is a subgroup.

Let
$$H = H_1 + H_2 + \ldots + H_h$$

and consider the $(1, 1)$-correspondence

$$H_i' \longleftrightarrow P^{-1}H_iP$$

between the elements of H' and H. An equation of the form

$$H_iH_j = H_k$$

then implies that

$$P^{-1}(H_iH_j)P = P^{-1}H_kP,$$
$$(P^{-1}H_iP)(P^{-1}H_jP) = P^{-1}H_kP,$$
$$H_i'H_j' = H_k',$$

which proves that the two groups are isomorphic (p. 19).

12. Lagrange's Theorem. We begin by a more detailed study of the complexes HX, where H is a subgroup but X is now any element of G, not necessarily contained in H.

LEMMA 2. *If H is a subgroup and if* R *and* S *are any two elements of* G, *then the complexes* HR *and* HS *are identical if, and only if,* $RS^{-1} \subset H$; *otherwise they have no element in common.*

Similarly, the complexes RH *and* SH *are identical if, and only if,* $S^{-1}R \subset H$; *otherwise they have no element in common.*

Proof. Let $RS^{-1} = H$, where $H \subset H$. Then by Lemma 1,

$$H(RS^{-1}) = (HR)S^{-1} = H,$$

whence on multiplying by S,

$$HR = HS. \qquad . \qquad . \qquad . \qquad (2.18)$$

Conversely, let us suppose that (2.18) is fulfilled, i.e. that every element of HR is an element of HS, and vice versa ; if

$$H = I + H_2 + \ldots + H_h, \qquad . \qquad . \qquad (2.19)$$

a typical element of HR is H_iR ; any one of these elements, including IR, must be of the form HS where $H \subset H$; thus

$$IR = H_lS,$$
$$RS^{-1} = H_l \subset H.$$

Again, if HR and HS have an element in common, we have an equation of the form

$$H_iR = H_jS,$$

whence

$$RS^{-1} = H_i^{-1}H_j$$

where the right-hand side represents an element of H because H is a group (a closed set). It then follows from the first part of this proof that the complexes (2.18) are in fact identical.

We are now in a position to prove one of the oldest and most important theorems on groups.

THEOREM 3 (Lagrange). *If H is a subgroup of* G *where the orders of these groups are* h *and* g *respectively, then* h *is a factor of* g, *i.e.*

$$g = nh. \qquad . \qquad . \qquad . \qquad (2.20)$$

The integer n *is called the* **index** *of* H *in* G.

There exists a set of n *elements* R_1, R_2, . . . , R_n *in* G *such that*

$$G = HR_1 + HR_2 + \ldots + HR_n \qquad . \qquad . \quad (2.21)$$

and a set S_1, S_2, . . . , S_n *such that*

$$G = S_1H + S_2H + \ldots + S_nH. \qquad . \qquad . \quad (2.22)$$

The equations (2.21) *and* (2.22) *are respectively referred to as the decompositions of* G *into* right-hand *or* left-hand **cosets** * *relative to* H.

Proof. The elements R_1, R_2, . . . , R_n will be determined one by one. Let R_1 be any element of H, e.g., since H is a group, we may put $R_1 = I$. We then have

$$HR_1 = H.$$

If $H \neq G$, there exists an element R_2 of G which is not contained in H. The complexes H and HR_2 cannot be identical because one of the elements of HR_2 is IR_2, i.e. R_2, which is not an element of H. Thus, by Lemma 2, the complexes H and HR_2 have no element in common. Hence the complex

$$HR_1 + HR_2 \qquad . \qquad . \qquad . \quad (2.23)$$

contains $2h$ distinct elements of G. If there is an element R_3 of G which is not contained in (2.23), then HR_3, which includes R_3 among its elements, differs from H and HR_2 and therefore has no element in common with either of these complexes. Hence

$$HR_1 + HR_2 + HR_3 \qquad . \qquad . \quad (2.24)$$

consists of $3h$ elements of G. If this accounts for all the elements of G we have established the decomposition required $(n = 3)$; in the contrary case, there exists an element R_4 of G which is not contained in (2.24). We then infer that the whole complex HR_4 consists in fact of new elements. Thus at every stage of the proof we

---

* Sometimes referred to as **associate complexes**.

D

discover that either the group G has been exhausted or that at least h elements are still left. Since G is finite, this process must come to an end after n steps, say; and we have arrived at the result that

$$G = HR_1 + HR_2 + \ldots + HR_n, \qquad . \qquad . \quad (2.25)$$

where each of the complexes on the right contains h elements and no two complexes have an element in common. Thus on comparing the number of elements on both sides of (2.25) we find that

$$g = h + h + \ldots + h,$$
$$g = hn.$$

The elements R_i are not uniquely determined; for if H is any element of H whatsoever,

$$HR_i = (HH)R_i = H(HR_i),$$

so that, for our purposes, R_i may be replaced by HR_i.

On the other hand, the aggregate of all distinct complexes of the form HX, where X is any element of G, is of course completely determined by the groups G and H. It is true that we can formally write down g such complexes, namely,

$$HG_1, \quad HG_2, \ldots, \quad HG_g, \quad . \qquad . \qquad . \quad (2.26)$$

where

$$G = G_1 + G_2 + \ldots + G_g.$$

However, if

$$G_\alpha = HG_\beta,$$

where H is any one of the h elements of H, we have

$$HG_\alpha = HG_\beta,$$

so that each complex in (2.26) is repeated h times and only g/h ($= n$) of them are distinct. The n complexes

$$HR_1, \quad HR_2, \ldots, \quad HR_n, . \qquad . \qquad . \quad (2.27)$$

which occur on the right-hand side of (2.25) are actually distinct, and it is for this reason that (2.27) is called a *complete system of right-hand cosets of* G *relative to* H ; it includes as its first member the group H itself. The remaining complexes are not groups because they do not contain the element I.

Similar remarks apply to the *left-hand* cosets YH. By repeating the arguments which led to (2.25) we arrive at a decomposition of the form

$$G = S_1 H + S_2 H + \ldots + S_n H \qquad . \qquad . \quad (2.28)$$

yielding, as before, the equation

$$g = hn.$$

One of the terms on the right-hand side of (2.28) is equal to H, say

$$S_1 H = H,$$

where S_1 is any element of H, e.g., $S_1 = I$.

It should be noted that not only the order h of the subgroup H but also its index $n (= g/h)$ is a factor of g.

Example. In the group of order 6

$$G : I, A, B, C, D, E$$

given in Table 1 (p. 12) the complex

$$H = I + C$$

forms a subgroup of order 2 since $C^2 = I$; or, if we wish to use Criterion 2 (p. 33), because

$$H^2 = (I + C)(I + C) = I + C + C + C^2 = I + C + C + I$$
$$= H + H = H.$$

The index of H in G is 3 $(= 6/2)$ and the elements R_1, R_2, R_3 in (2.25) may be taken as I, A, B respectively ; in fact

$$G = H + HA + HB = (I + C) + (I + C)A + (I + C)B$$
$$= I + C + A + D + B + E.$$

We shall now derive some simple consequences of Lagrange's theorem.

Corollary 1.   *If G is a group of order g, the order of every element of G is a factor of g.*

Proof.   Let A be an element of G of order a ; then G contains the elements

$$I, A, A^2, \ldots, A^{a-1}, \quad (A^a = I)$$

which form a cyclic subgroup of order a. Hence, by Lagrange's theorem, a is a factor of g.

Example.   In the group of Table 1 (p. 12) the elements can only be of orders 1, 2, 3 or 6. In fact, it is easily verified that the orders of I, A, B, C, D, E are 1, 3, 3, 2, 2, 2 respectively.

Corollary 2.   *A group of prime order has no proper subgroups and is necessarily cyclic.*

Proof.   If the order of the group is a prime number p, the order of a subgroup must be either 1 or p, i.e. the subgroup consists either of the single element I or contains all p elements of the group.

If A is an element other than I, its order, being greater than 1, is necessarily equal to p. Hence the p elements $I, A, A^2, \ldots, A^{p-1}$ $(A^p = I)$ are all the elements of G in some order.

13. Subgroups of a Cyclic Group.   A cyclic group

$$G = I + A + \ldots + A^{g-1}, \quad (A^g = I)$$

which is generated by the element A, will simply be denoted by

$$G = \{A.\}$$

We can obtain complete information about all its possible subgroups from

Theorem 4.   *All subgroups of a cyclic group are cyclic. If $\{A\}$ is a cyclic group of order g, then corresponding to every divisor h of g there exists one, and only one, subgroup of order h, which may be generated by $A^{g/h}$.*

Proof. (i) Let $g = hn$. The elements

$$I, A^n, A^{2n}, \ldots, A^{(h-1)n} \quad . \quad\quad . \quad\quad . \quad (2.29)$$

are distinct, since an equality between any two of them would lead to a relation

$$A^{ln} = I,$$

where

$$0 < ln < hn(= g).$$

This would contradict the assumption that A is of order g. The elements (2.29) form a cyclic subgroup

$$\{A^n\}$$

of order h, as required.

(ii) Conversely, suppose that

$$H = I + A_1 + A_2 + \ldots + A_{h-1} \quad . \quad\quad . \quad (2.30)$$

is a subgroup of order h of $\{A\}$. Since A_i is an element of $\{A\}$, it must be of the form

$$A_i = A^{\lambda_i},$$

where λ_i is a certain integer such that

$$0 < \lambda_i < g.$$

As H is of order h, the hth power of each of its elements is equal to the unit element. Thus

$$A_i^h = A^{h\lambda_i} = I.$$

It follows that $h\lambda_i$ is a multiple of g (Chapter I, Theorem 3, p. 22), say

$$h\lambda_i = k_i g = k_i hn,$$

whence

$$\lambda_i = k_i n.$$

Hence

$$A_i = A^{\lambda_i} = (A^n)^{k_i},$$

which shows that each element of (2.30) is in fact a power of A^n. But we have seen that not more than h of these powers are distinct, namely the h elements listed in (2.29). Hence the h elements of H in (2.30) are the same as those in (2.29). Thus

$$H = \{A^n\},$$

which proves the theorem.

We have seen (Corollary 2, p. 38) that groups of prime order have no proper subgroups. The converse of this proposition is also true, namely

THEOREM 5. *Every finite group of composite order has proper subgroups.*

Proof. When the group is not cyclic, no single element generates the whole group ; hence if A is any element other than I, then $\{A\}$ is a *proper* subgroup.

In the case of cyclic groups of composite order the existence of proper subgroups is safeguarded by Theorem 4.

14. Intersection and generators. The elements that are common to a number of complexes

$$K, L, \ldots \qquad . \qquad . \qquad . \qquad (2.31)$$

of G form a complex

$$D = K \cap L \cap \qquad . \qquad . \qquad . \qquad (2.32)$$

which is called the **intersection** of $K, L, \ldots$. When the intersection is empty, i.e. when the complexes (2.31) have no element in common, we write

$$0 = K \cap L \cap \ldots.$$

Next, we shall show that, if P and Q are any elements of G, then

$$PDQ = PKQ \cap PLQ \cap \ldots \qquad . \qquad . \qquad (2.33)$$

where PDQ is to be interpreted as zero if D is zero. In order to prove (2.33) let

$$PKQ \cap PLQ \cap \ldots = D'$$

If Z' is any element of D', i.e. if

$$Z' \subset PKQ, \quad Z' \subset PLQ, \ldots,$$

we have

$$P^{-1}Z'Q^{-1} \subset K, \quad P^{-1}Z'Q^{-1} \subset L, \ldots,$$

which means that $P^{-1}Z'Q^{-1}$ belongs to D; thus we have shown that $P^{-1}D'Q^{-1} \subset D$, or (see p. 30)

$$D' \subset PDQ. \quad \quad \quad \quad (2.34)$$

In particular, if D is empty so is D'.

Conversely, if Z is any element of D, it follows that PZQ is an element of D', so that

$$PDQ \subset D'. \quad \quad \quad \quad (2.35)$$

The two relations (2.34) and (2.35) together imply (see p. 30) that

$$PDQ = D',$$

which proves (2.33).

We note that, in particular,

$$P^{-1}DP = P^{-1}KP \cap P^{-1}LP \cap \ldots \quad \quad (2.36)$$

When the complexes $K, L, \ldots$ are *subgroups*, their intersection is never empty, as all subgroups have at least the unit element in common. In such cases the intersection is in many respects analogous to the **highest common factor** (**H.C.F.**) of integers and is often called by that name.

THEOREM 6. *The intersection of subgroups* $A, B, C, \ldots$ *is a subgroup* (*proper or improper*) *of each of the groups* $A, B, C, \ldots$.

Proof. Let $D = A \cap B \cap C \cap \ldots$ By definition we have

$$D \subset A, \quad D \subset B, \quad D \subset C, \ldots$$

and it only remains for us to prove that D is a group, i.e. that it is closed. If X and Y belong to D, we have

$$X \subset A, \quad X \subset B, \quad X \subset C, \ldots$$

and

$$Y \subset A, \quad Y \subset B, \quad Y \subset C, \ldots$$

Since A is a group it follows that $XY \subset A$, and, similarly, that $XY \subset B$, $XY \subset C$, ... Hence

$$XY \subset D,$$

which means that D is closed.

We now turn to another method of constructing subgroups of a given group G. Let $A, B, C, \ldots$ be any elements of G and consider the set of all possible products consisting of a finite number of factors selected from these elements with or without repetitions, e.g. $BACA^2B$. Let the aggregate of all products obtained in this way be denoted by

$$M = \{A, B, C, \ldots\}.$$

It is clear that M is closed, because on multiplying two products of a finite number of factors we get another such product. Hence M is a (proper or improper) subgroup of G. We say that the elements $A, B, C, \ldots$ form a set of **generators** of M. If M' is any subgroup containing the elements $A, B, C, \ldots$, it necessarily contains all their products and hence also the subgroup M. Thus M may be described as the smallest subgroup of G containing $A, B, C, \ldots$.

Our present notation agrees with that used on p. 2, since in any group the set of all elements may be regarded as a set of generators.

More generally, we may construct a subgroup

$$M = \{K, L, \ldots\} \qquad . \qquad . \qquad . \quad (2.37)$$

generated by a set of complexes $K, L, \ldots$.

Let

$$K = \{K_1, K_2, \ldots\}, \quad L = \{L_1, L_2, \ldots\}.$$

The subgroup (2.37) is then defined as

$$M = \{K_1, K_2, \ldots, L_1, L_2 \ldots\}. \qquad . \qquad . \quad (2.38)$$

Thus a typical element of M is

$$X = A_1 A_2 \ldots A_s,$$

where each A is an element of one of the complexes K, L, ...

Let P be any element of G and consider the group

$$M' = \{P^{-1}KP, P^{-1}LP, \ldots\}. \qquad . \qquad . \quad (2.39)$$

Since

$$P^{-1}XP = (P^{-1}A_1P)(P^{-1}A_2P) \ldots (P^{-1}A_sP),$$

we infer that $P^{-1}XP$ belongs to M', as it is a product of elements from $P^{-1}KP$, $P^{-1}LP$, . . . Thus we have shown that

$$P^{-1}MP \subset M'. \qquad . \qquad . \qquad . \quad (2.40)$$

On reversing the rôles of M and M' where P is to be replaced by P^{-1}, we arrive at the result that

$$PM'P^{-1} \subset M,$$

which together with (2.40) implies that

$$P^{-1}MP = \{P^{-1}KP, P^{-1}LP, \ldots\}. \qquad . \qquad . \quad (2.41)$$

Thus the group of order 6, whose abstract multiplication table was given on p. 12, can be generated by the two elements A and C, in terms of which each of the six elements can be expressed, namely

$$I = C^2(=A^3), \quad A = A, \quad B = A^2, \quad C = C, \quad D = CA, \quad E = AC.$$

We may therefore denote that group simply by

$$\{A, C\}.$$

However, it must not be supposed that the set of generators is uniquely determined ; for example, in the present case we have

$$\{A, C\} = \{B, D\},$$

since A and C may in turn be expressed in terms of B and D, namely

$$A = B^2, \quad C = DB.$$

It is obvious that every finite group can be generated by a finite number of elements. We say that *the elements*

$$G_1, G_2, \ldots, G_m \qquad \qquad (2.42)$$

are **independent** *if none of them can be expressed in terms of the others, i.e. if* G_i *is not an element of* $\{G_1, G_2, \ldots, G_{i-1}, G_{i+1}, \ldots, G_m\}$. Suppose that the elements $G_1, G_2, \ldots, G_m$ generate **G** so that we have

$$\mathsf{G} = \{G_1, G_2, \ldots, G_m\}. \qquad \qquad (2.43)$$

We may evidently omit any generator that depends on the others without changing the resulting group (2.43). In fact we can always reduce a given set of generators until they become independent. *Hence every finite group possesses at least one set of independent generators.*

The independence of the generating elements does not preclude the existence of certain relations between them. Thus, returning to our previous example, we can easily verify from the multiplication table (p. 12) that

$$AC = CA^2, \quad \text{or} \quad (AC)^2 = I. \qquad . \qquad (2.44)$$

Nevertheless, the elements A and C are independent, as it is clearly impossible to express A in terms of C, or vice versa. An equation like (2.44) is called a **defining relation**. *It is often convenient to specify a group by a set of independent generators, for which the associative law is assumed, together with a system of defining relations sufficient to construct the complete multiplication table.*

Thus the group of Table 1 may be given by

$$A^3 = C^2 = (AC)^2 = I, \qquad . \qquad . \qquad (2.45)$$

where the first two relations express that A and C are of orders 3 and 2 respectively. Using only the information contained in (2.45) and the associative law, we might argue as follows : the six elements

$$I, A, A^2, C, CA, CA^2 \qquad . \qquad . \qquad (2.46)$$

are certainly *distinct*, as any equality between them would immediately result in a contradiction; e.g. if A were equal to CA^2, it would follow that $A^{-1} = C$, which is incompatible with the assumption that A and C are independent. On the other hand, the elements (2.46) form a *closed* set in virtue of (2.45); e.g.

$$(CA)(CA^2) = C(AC)A^2 = CCA^2A^2 = C^2A^4 = A,$$
$$A^2C \quad = A(AC) \quad = ACA^2 \quad = CA^4 = CA,$$

and so on, a factor C being systematically moved to the left until the product is seen to be identical with one of the elements (2.46). The complete multiplication table of these six elements is as follows:

	I	A	A^2	C	CA	CA^2
I	I	A	A^2	C	CA	CA^2
A	A	A^2	I	CA^2	C	CA
A^2	A^2	I	A	CA	CA^2	C
C	C	CA	CA^2	I	A	A^2
CA	CA	CA^2	C	A^2	I	A
CA^2	CA^2	C	CA	A	A^2	I

Table 7

The reader will have no difficulty in convincing himself that this table is identical with Table 1 (p. 12), provided that the elements (2.46) are renamed

$$I, A, B, C, D, E$$

respectively.

15. The Direct Product. From any two abstract groups G and H of orders g and h respectively, a new group of order gh may be derived, which is denoted by

$$G \times H \quad \text{or} \quad H \times G$$

and is called the **direct product** of G and H. Its elements are all possible *pairs of elements*, one from G and one from H, and may be written

$$(G, H) \quad \text{or} \quad G \times H,$$

where G and H are typical elements of G and H respectively. As regards the law of composition it is stipulated that

$$(G_1, H_1)(G_2, H_2) = (G_1 G_2, H_1 H_2). \qquad . \quad (2.47)$$

This rule automatically establishes the *associative law* for the group so derived. The *unit element* of $\mathsf{G} \times \mathsf{H}$ is the product of the unit elements of G and H. We note that

$$(G, H)^{-1} = (G^{-1}, H^{-1}).$$

The direct product of Abelian groups is Abelian.

Suppose that every element of a group F is of the form GH, where G and H are elements of subgroups G and H of F possessing the following properties :

    (i) every element of G commutes with every element of H,

    (ii) G and H have only the element I in common.

Then F is isomorphic with $\mathsf{G} \times \mathsf{H}$. For the correspondence $(G, H)' = GH$ between $\mathsf{G} \times \mathsf{H}$ and F is $(1, 1)$ because $GH = G_1 H_1$ implies that $G^{-1}{}_1 G = H_1 H^{-1} = J$, say. J belongs to both G and H and hence is I. Thus $G = G_1$, $H = H_1$. Furthermore, the correspondence is an isomorphism because

$$(GG_1, HH_1)' = GG_1 HH_1 = GHG_1 H_1 = (G, H)'(G_1, H_1)'.$$

More generally we can define the direct product of k groups ; it is denoted by

$$\mathsf{G}_1 \times \mathsf{G}_2 \times \ldots \times \mathsf{G}_k \,;$$

a typical element may be written

$$G_1 G_2 \ldots G_k \qquad . \qquad . \qquad . \qquad (2.48)$$

where G_λ is a typical element of G_λ. The factors in (2.48) commute with one another and are independent in the sense that

$$G_1 G_2 \ldots G_k = I$$

if, and only if, each G_λ is equal to the unit element.

Example. The least positive residues prime to the modulus 15 are

$$1, 2, 4, 7, 8, 11, 13, 14. \quad . \quad . \quad . \quad (2.49)$$

They form an Abelian group of order 8 (pp. 15-18) which, as we shall now show, is equal to the direct product of two cyclic groups generated by the elements 2 and 11 respectively. In fact the residue 2 generates a cyclic group of order 4, namely

$$C_4 : 1, 2, 4, 8 ; \quad 2^4 = 16 \equiv 1 \text{ (mod. 15)}.$$

Similarly, 11 generates a cyclic group of order 2,

$$C_2 : 1, 11 ; \quad 11^2 = 121 \equiv 1 \text{ (mod. 15)}.$$

The elements of $C_4 \times C_2$ are obtained by multiplying the elements of C_4 by those of C_2, thus

$$C_4 \times C_2 : 1, 2, 4, 8, 11, 22, 44, 88.$$

On being reduced to the least positive residue relative to 15, these numbers become

$$1, 2, 4, 8, 11, 7, 14, 13,$$

which agrees with (2.49). The group is therefore isomorphic with $C_4 \times C_2$.

The following lemma will be used in the next section, but is also of some intrinsic interest :

LEMMA 3. *If each element of G, other than the unit element, is of order 2, then G is Abelian and isomorphic with*

$$C_2 \times C_2 \times \ldots \times C_2.$$

Its order is a power of 2.

Proof. The proposition is obviously true when G is the (only) group of order 2. Suppose then that the order of G is greater than 2 and let A and B be any two distinct elements other than I. We have

$$A^2 = I, \quad \text{i.e.} \quad A = A^{-1}$$

and

$$B^2 = I, \quad \text{i.e.} \quad B = B^{-1}.$$

Next consider the element AB.   Evidently $AB \neq I$, or else $A = B^{-1} = B$.   Hence, by hypothesis, AB is of order 2, i.e.

$$I = (AB)^2 = A(BA)B,$$
$$BA = A^{-1}B^{-1} = AB,$$

which proves that **G** is Abelian.

Since **G** is finite, it possesses a finite set of independent generators, say

$$A_1, A_2, \ldots, A_k.$$

As the group is Abelian, powers of the same element may be collected in any product.   Thus the general element of **G** can be written

$$G = A_1^{\alpha_1} A_2^{\alpha_2} \ldots A_k^{\alpha_k},$$

where $\alpha_i = 0$ or 1 $(i = 1, 2, \ldots, k)$, because the square of each element is equal to I.   Hence

$$\mathsf{G} = \{A_1\} \times \{A_2\} \times \ldots \times \{A_k\},$$

and the order of **G** is

$$g = 2 \times 2 \times \ldots \times 2 = 2^k.$$

16. Survey of Groups up to Order 8.   No successful method has yet been discovered for constructing all possible abstract groups of preassigned order, nor do we know in advance how many such groups exist, except in a few simple cases.

The modest means with which we have so far furnished the reader will, however, suffice to give a complete list of groups up to order 8.   We shall specify each of these groups by a set of defining relations.   Since groups of prime order have already been discussed (Corollary 2, p. 38), it only remains for us to consider in more detail the cases in which

$$g = 4 \quad \text{or} \quad 6 \quad \text{or} \quad 8.$$

There are two groups of order 4, *both of them Abelian.*

For if $g = 4$, any element, other than I, can only be of order 4 or 2 (Corollary 1, p. 38).

(1) If G contains an element A of order 4, this element generates G ; in fact the four elements of G can be written

$$I, A, A^2, A^3, (A^4 = I) \quad . \quad . \quad . \quad (2.50)$$

and we have $G = C_4$, a cyclic group of order 4.

(2) Next, suppose that every element, except I, is of order 2. Hence by Lemma 3 (p. 47)

$$G = C_2 \times C_2,$$

i.e. G is generated by two elements A and B, and the four elements of G can be written

$$I, A, B, AB, \quad . \quad . \quad . \quad (2.51)$$

where

$$A^2 = B^2 = I, \quad AB = BA . \quad . \quad . \quad (2.52)$$

This group is called the **four-group** or **quadratic group** (F. Klein's " *Vierergruppe* ") ; it is often denoted by V.

There being no other possibilities, we conclude that *any group of order 4 is isomorphic either with* C_4 *or with* V. We have already encountered both these groups in Chapter I. In fact, Table 5 (p. 20) represents C_4 since $B = A^2$, $C = A^3$, while Table 6 (p. 21) corresponds to V, provided that we write $C = AB$.

There are two groups of order 6, one cyclic and one non-Abelian.

(1) If G possesses an element A of order 6, then

$$G = \{A\} = C_6.$$

(2) Next, suppose there is no element of order 6 ; the order of every element, other than I, is therefore either 2 or 3 (Corollary 1, p. 38). Since the order of G is not a power of 2, not all its elements can be of order 2 (Lemma 3, p. 47). Hence there exists at least one element A of order 3, so that

$$I, A, A^2 \quad (A^3 = I) \quad . \quad . \quad . \quad (2.53)$$

are three distinct elements of G. If B is a further element, it is easy to see that the six elements

$$I, A, A^2, B, AB, A^2B \quad . \quad . \quad . \quad (2.54)$$

are distinct, because an equality between any two of them would immediately lead to a contradiction ; e.g. $A^2B = A$ would imply that $B = A^{-1} = A^2$, whereas we had supposed that B was not one of the elements (2.53). If the set (2.54) is to form a group of order 6, the condition of closure must be fulfilled. In particular, B^2 must be equal to one of the elements (2.54) ; as we cannot have an equation of the form $B^2 = A^iB$ (it would be incompatible with the independence of A and B), there are only the following three possibilities

$$\text{(a) } B^2 = I, \quad \text{(b) } B^2 = A, \quad \text{(c) } B^2 = A^2. \quad . \quad (2.55)$$

In the last two cases B cannot be of order 2 and hence must be of order 3, i.e. $B^3 = I$; but on postmultiplying (b) or (c) by B we should then get $I = AB$ or $I = A^2B$, neither of which can possibly be true. Thus (a) must hold, i.e.

$$B^2 = I. \quad . \quad . \quad . \quad (2.56)$$

Next consider the element BA ; it must be contained in (2.54). As it cannot be equal to B or to a power of A, we are left with the alternatives

$$\text{(a) } BA = AB, \quad \text{(b) } BA = A^2B. \quad . \quad . \quad (2.57)$$

In the first case G would be Abelian. Hence

$$(AB)^2 = A^2B^2 = A^2 \neq I, \quad (AB)^3 = A^3B^3 = B \neq I,$$

and the element AB would be of order 6, contrary to the assumption made at the beginning of this section. Thus we are forced to conclude that

$$BA = A^2B, \quad \text{i.e. } (AB)^2 = I.$$

Subject to the associative law being confirmed, the relations

$$A^3 = B^2 = (AB)^2 = I \quad . \quad . \quad . \quad (2.58)$$

completely define the group which we first introduced in Table 1 and have repeatedly discussed since, especially in Table 7 (see pp. 44 and 45). There are no other groups of order 6.

There are five groups of order 8 *of which three are Abelian and two are non-Abelian.*

Three Abelian groups of order 8 are easily written down, namely:

(1) $C_8 = \{A\}$, where $A^8 = I$ (Table 8, p. 54).
(2) $C_4 \times C_2 = \{A, B\}$, where $A^4 = B^2 = I$, $AB = BA$
                                       (Table 9, p. 54).
(3) $C_2 \times C_2 \times C_2 = \{A, B, C\}$, where $A^2 = B^2 = C^2 = I$,
        $AB = BA, BC = CB, CA = AC$ (Table 10, p. 55).

In searching for further groups of order 8 we may assume that the maximum order of elements is less than 8 and greater than 2 (Lemma 3, p. 47). Hence there is at least one element A of order 4, i.e.

$$A^4 = I, \qquad . \quad . \quad . \quad . \quad (2.59)$$

and the order of any element other than I is either 2 or 4.

If B is an element not contained in $\{A\}$, we can write the eight elements of the group in the form

$$I, A, A^2, A^3, B, AB, A^2B, A^3B. \quad . \qquad (2.60)$$

The condition of closure demands that B^2 be one of these elements, which in fact must be one of the first four, since B is independent of A. But the equations

$$B^2 = A \quad \text{or} \quad B^2 = A^3$$

are impossible, as they would imply that the order of B was neither 2 nor 4. Thus there remain only two possibilities, namely

$$(4) \ \ B^2 = I \quad \text{or} \quad (5) \ \ B^2 = A^2.$$

(4) Assume that $B^2 = I$. The product BA must be equal to one of the last three elements of (2.60).

E

(a) If $BA = AB$, we obtain the Abelian group which has already been noted under (2).

(b) The relation $BA = A^2B$, which is equivalent to

$$B^{-1}A^2B = A,$$

is impossible, as on squaring we should arrive at the result

$$A^2 = (B^{-1}A^2B)(B^{-1}A^2B) = B^{-1}A^4B = B^{-1}IB = I,$$

in contradiction to (2.59). Thus we are forced to conclude that

(c) $\qquad BA = A^3B, \quad \text{or} \quad (AB)^2 = I.$

The group which is defined by the relations

$$A^4 = B^2 = (AB)^2 = I \quad . \quad . \quad . \quad (2.61)$$

is called the **dihedral group** *of order* 8 (Table 11, p. 55), or **octic group**.

It belongs to a class of groups which we shall discuss later (p. 90), when the associative law will be confirmed.

(5) Let $B^2 = A^2$. In this case B is, like A, of order 4. Again, BA must be equal to one of the last three elements of (2.60).

(a) If $BA = AB$, the group is Abelian. On putting $C = AB^{-1}$ we see that C is of order 2. Also, since $B = C^{-1}A$, A and C may be taken as generating elements of the group, which is therefore of the form $C_4 \times C_2$ (type (2)).

(b) The relation $BA = A^2B$, i.e. $BA = B^2B = B^3$, is impossible, as it would imply that $A = B^2 = A^2$, which is clearly absurd. Thus we must assume that

(c) $\qquad BA = A^3B.$

The relations

$$A^4 = I, \quad A^2 = B^2, \quad BA = A^3B \quad . \quad . \quad (2.62)$$

do in fact define what is called the **quaternion group** (Table 12, p. 55).

In order to explain this name we remind the reader that a quaternion is a *hypercomplex number*

$$a_0 + a_1 i + a_2 j + a_3 k,$$

where the coefficients a_0, a_1, a_2, a_3, are *real* numbers, and the four *units*

$$1, i, j, k \qquad . \quad . \quad . \quad . \quad (2.63)$$

satisfy the relations

$$i^2 = j^2 = -1, \quad ij = -ji = k. \qquad . \quad . \quad (2.64)$$

If we are only interested in the multiplicative properties of the symbols (2.63), we must interpret -1 as i^2, and the rules (2.64), which govern the algebra of quaternions, become $k = ij$ and

$$i^4 = 1, \quad i^2 = j^2, \quad ji = i^3 j. \quad . \qquad . \quad . \quad (2.65)$$

In this form they are indeed identical with (2.62), apart from the notation.

The reader will have no difficulty in demonstrating that the quaternion group is isomorphic with the groups of matrices generated by

$$A_2 = \begin{bmatrix} 0 & \sqrt{-1} \\ \sqrt{-1} & 0 \end{bmatrix} \quad \text{and} \quad B_2 = \begin{bmatrix} 0 & 1 \\ -1 & 0 \end{bmatrix},$$

or by

$$A_4 = \begin{bmatrix} 0 & 1 & 0 & 0 \\ -1 & 0 & 0 & 0 \\ 0 & 0 & 0 & -1 \\ 0 & 0 & 1 & 0 \end{bmatrix} \quad \text{and} \quad B_4 = \begin{bmatrix} 0 & 0 & 1 & 0 \\ 0 & 0 & 0 & 1 \\ -1 & 0 & 0 & 0 \\ 0 & -1 & 0 & 0 \end{bmatrix}.$$

This affords an indirect verification of the associative law, which is known to be true for all matrices.

The quaternion group is an instance of a **dicyclic group**. These are groups of order $4m$ defined by

$$A^{2m} = I \quad , \quad A^m = (AB)^2 = B^2 \quad .$$

The elements of a dicyclic group may be written

$$I, A, \ldots, \quad A^{2m-1}, \quad B, \quad AB, \ldots, \quad A^{2m-1}B.$$

The square of every element which does not belong to $\{A\}$, is equal to B^2. For since

$$ABA = B,$$
$$(A^xB)^2 = A^xBA^xB = A^{x-1}(ABA)A^{x-1}B = A^{x-1}BA^{x-1}B$$
$$= A^{x-2}(ABA)A^{x-2}B = A^{x-2}BA^{x-2}B$$
$$= \ldots = A^0BA^0B = B^2.$$

To emphasize the structural difference of the five possible groups of order 8 we append their complete multiplication tables:

$$\mathsf{C}_8 = \{A\}, \quad A^8 = I.$$

	I	A	A^2	A^3	A^4	A^5	A^6	A^7
I	I	A	A^2	A^3	A^4	A^5	A^6	A^7
A	A	A^2	A^3	A^4	A^5	A^6	A^7	I
A^2	A^2	A^3	A^4	A^5	A^6	A^7	I	A
A^3	A^3	A^4	A^5	A^6	A^7	I	A	A^2
A^4	A^4	A^5	A^6	A^7	I	A	A^2	A^3
A^5	A^5	A^6	A^7	I	A	A^2	A^3	A^4
A^6	A^6	A^7	I	A	A^2	A^3	A^4	A^5
A^7	A^7	I	A	A^2	A^3	A^4	A^5	A^6

Table 8

$$\mathsf{C}_4 \times \mathsf{C}_2 = \{A, B\}, \quad A^4 = B^2 = I.$$

	I	A	A^2	A^3	B	AB	A^2B	A^3B
I	I	A	A^2	A^3	B	AB	A^2B	A^3B
A	A	A^2	A^3	I	AB	A^2B	A^3B	B
A^2	A^2	A^3	I	A	A^2B	A^3B	B	AB
A^3	A^3	I	A	A^2	A^3B	B	AB	A^2B
B	B	AB	A^2B	A^3B	I	A	A^2	A^3
AB	AB	A^2B	A^3B	B	A	A^2	A^3	I
A^2B	A^2B	A^3B	B	AB	A^2	A^3	I	A
A^3B	A^3B	B	AB	A^2B	A^3	I	A	A^2

Table 9

$C_2 \times C_2 \times C_2 = \{A, B, C\}, \quad A^2 = B^2 = C^2 = I.$

	I	A	B	C	AB	AC	BC	ABC
I	I	A	B	C	AB	AC	BC	ABC
A	A	I	AB	AC	B	C	ABC	BC
B	B	AB	I	BC	A	ABC	C	AC
C	C	AC	BC	I	ABC	A	B	AB
AB	AB	B	A	ABC	I	BC	AC	C
AC	AC	C	ABC	A	BC	I	AB	B
BC	BC	ABC	C	B	AC	AB	I	A
ABC	ABC	BC	AC	AB	C	B	A	I

Table 10

Dihedral Group $A^4 = B^2 = I, \quad BA = A^3B.$

	I	A	A^2	A^3	B	AB	A^2B	A^3B
I	I	A	A^2	A^3	B	AB	A^2B	A^3B
A	A	A^2	A^3	I	AB	A^2B	A^3B	B
A^2	A^2	A^3	I	A	A^2B	A^3B	B	AB
A^3	A^3	I	A	A^2	A^3B	B	AB	A^2B
B	B	A^3B	A^2B	AB	I	A^3	A^2	A
AB	AB	B	A^3B	A^2B	A	I	A^3	A^2
A^2B	A^2B	AB	B	A^3B	A^2	A	I	A^3
A^3B	A^3B	A^2B	AB	B	A^3	A^2	A	1

Table 11

Quaternion Group $A^4 = I, \quad A^2 = B^2, \quad BA = A^3B.$

	I	A	A^2	A^3	B	AB	A^2B	A^3B
J	I	A	A^2	A^3	B	AB	A^2B	A^3B
A	A	A^2	A^3	I	AB	A^2B	A^3B	B
A^2	A^2	A^3	I	A	A^2B	A^3B	B	AB
A^3	A^3	I	A	A^2	A^3B	B	AB	A^2B
B	B	A^3B	A^2B	AB	A^2	A	I	A^3
AB	AB	B	A^3B	A^2B	A^3	A^2	A	I
A^2B	A^2B	AB	B	A^3B	I	A^3	A^2	A
A^3B	A^3B	A^2B	AB	B	A	I	A^3	A^2

Table 12

17. The Product Theorem. At the beginning of this chapter (2.6) we defined the product of two complexes, *K* and *L*. We shall now examine the case in which both these complexes are *subgroups* of *G*. It will appear that the product of two subgroups (when both are regarded as complexes) is not always a subgroup.

THEOREM 7 (Product Theorem). *If A and B are subgroups of orders* a *and* b *respectively, with an intersection* (H.C.F.) *of order* d, *then the complex*

$$C = AB$$

contains exactly ab/d *distinct elements; and C is a group if, and only if, A and B commute.*

Proof. (i) Since *A* and *B* are groups, their intersection *D* is a subgroup of either group (Theorem 6, p. 41), and we can decompose *B* into cosets relative to *D*, thus

$$B = DB_1 + DB_2 + \ldots + DB_n, \qquad . \qquad . \quad (2.66)$$

where $n = b/d$ and

$$DB_i \neq DB_j, \quad \text{if } i \neq j. \quad . \qquad . \qquad (2.67)$$

Multiplying (2.66) on the left by *A*, we obtain

$$AB = ADB_1 + ADB_2 + \ldots + ADB_n.$$

Since *D* is contained in *A*, it follows from the Corollary on p. 32 that $AD = A$, and therefore

$$AB = AB_1 + AB_2 + \ldots + AB_n. \qquad . \qquad (2.68)$$

Each complex AB_i contains *a* distinct elements, and no two of these complexes have an element in common; for, if they had, we should get an equation of the form

$$A_\alpha B_i = A_\beta B_j, \quad (i \neq j)$$

where A_α and A_β are certain elements of *A*. Hence it would follow that

$$A_\beta^{-1} A_\alpha = B_j B_i^{-1}. \qquad . \qquad . \qquad (2.69)$$

Since A is a group, the left-hand side of (2.69) is an element of A; similarly, the right-hand side represents an element of B. This element would therefore be common to A and B, i.e. it would belong to the intersection D. Hence, by Lemma 1, p. 32, we should have

$$D(B_j B_i^{-1}) = D,$$
$$DB_j = DB_i$$

in contradiction to (2.67). Thus we conclude that the complexes AB_i in (2.68) have no elements in common and therefore contain a total of

$$na = \frac{b}{d}a$$

distinct elements. This proves the first part of the theorem. On interchanging A and B we note that *the complexes AB and BA (where A and B are groups) always contain the same number of elements even when $AB \neq BA$.*

(ii) Next, suppose that the complex $C = AB$ is in fact a group. If A and B are any elements of A and B respectively, we have $A^{-1} \subset A$, $B^{-1} \subset B$ and therefore

$$A^{-1}B^{-1} \subset AB.$$

Since AB is a group it contains the reciprocal of $A^{-1}B^{-1}$, i.e.

$$(A^{-1}B^{-1})^{-1} = BA \subset AB.$$

Now BA may be considered a typical element of BA. Hence we have proved that

$$BA \subset AB.$$

On the other hand, we have just seen that these two complexes contain the same number of distinct elements, so that BA cannot be a proper part of AB; it therefore follows that

$$BA = AB. \qquad . \qquad . \qquad . \qquad (2.70)$$

(iii) Conversely, if (2.70) is true, we have

$$C^2 = (AB)(AB) = A(BA)B = A(AB)B$$
$$= A^2B^2 = AB = C,$$

using Criterion 2 (p. 33) for the groups A and B ; and in virtue of the same Criterion we infer that C is a group. This completes the proof of the Product Theorem.

NOTE : This theorem is analogous to a well-known result of elementary arithmetic, namely that if a and b are any two integers whose H.C.F. and L.C.M. are d and c respectively, then

$$c = ab/d.$$

18. Decomposition relative to Two Subgroups. The decomposition of a group into cosets (Lagrange's Theorem, p. 34) was essentially based on the fact that two such cosets are either identical or else have no element in common. Whenever a set of complexes possesses this property, the elements of G can be divided into mutually exclusive classes.

The following generalization of the concept of cosets is due to G. Frobenius.*

Let A and B be subgroups of G (which need not be distinct) of orders a and b respectively, and consider complexes of the form

$$APB, AQB, \ldots$$

where P, Q, $\ldots$ are any elements of G. We shall prove that if two such complexes have one element in common, they are in fact identical. Indeed, let us suppose

$$A_1PB_1 = A_2QB_2,$$

where A_1, A_2 are elements of A and B_1, B_2 of B. On premultiplying by A and postmultiplying by B, we find that

$$AA_1PB_1B = AA_2QB_2B. \qquad . \qquad . \quad (2.71)$$

---

* *Sitzungsberichte Berlin*, 1895, pt. i, pp. 163-94.

Since A and B are groups we have (Lemma 1, p. 32)

$$AA_1 = AA_2 = A,$$
$$B_1B = B_2B = B,$$

whence (2.71) becomes

$$APB = AQB.$$

We note that the complex APB contains the element IPI, i.e. P.

Using these facts, we can obtain a decomposition of G in the following way : choose any element P_1 of G. If the complex AP_1B is less than G, let P_2 be an element not contained in it. Since P_2 is an element of AP_2B but not of AP_1B, these two complexes have no element in common, and we can segregate from G the complex

$$AP_1B + AP_2B. \qquad . \qquad . \qquad . \qquad (2.72)$$

If there is an element P_3 not yet accounted for, the complex AP_3B consists entirely of new elements and should be added to (2.72). We proceed in this way until the whole group G is exhausted. No further elements can then be found and we have an equation of the form

$$G = AP_1B + AP_2B + \ldots + AP_rB. \qquad . \qquad (2.73)$$

We say that G *has been decomposed relative to the subgroups* A *and* B.

In contrast to the resolution into cosets, the number of elements in the various terms on the right-hand side of (2.73) may vary and requires closer examination. Consider a typical complex

$$AP_\rho B = K_1 + K_2 + \ldots + K_l$$

which contains, say, l distinct elements of G. Evidently the complex

$$P_\rho^{-1}AP_\rho B = P_\rho^{-1}K_1 + P_\rho^{-1}K_2 + \ldots + P_\rho^{-1}K_l \qquad (2.74)$$

also contains l distinct elements, because if

$$P_\rho{}^{-1}K_\alpha = P_\rho{}^{-1}K_\beta$$

we should find that

$$K_\alpha = K_\beta,$$

and vice versa. Let

$$P_\rho{}^{-1}AP_\rho = A_\rho.$$

This is a subgroup which is isomorphic with A (Theorem 2, p. 33) and hence is of order a. The left-hand side of (2.74) can accordingly be regarded as the product of two groups, namely

$$A_\rho B.$$

On applying the Product Theorem (p. 56) we infer that

$$l = ab/d_\rho, \qquad . \qquad . \qquad . \qquad (2.75)$$

where d_ρ is the order of the intersection $A_\rho \cap B$.

We collect these results in the following theorem.

THEOREM 8 (Frobenius). *If A and B are subgroups of G of orders* a *and* b *respectively, G admits of a decomposition into mutually exclusive complexes relative to A and B, thus*

$$G = AP_1B + AP_2B + \ldots + AP_rB.$$

The complex $AP_\rho B$ contains ab/d_ρ *elements where* d_ρ *is the order of the intersection* $P_\rho{}^{-1}AP_\rho \cap B$.

COROLLARY. *On counting the number of elements in each term of (2.73) we obtain the relation*

$$g = \sum_{\rho=1}^{r} \frac{ab}{d_\rho}. \qquad . \qquad . \qquad . \qquad (2.76)$$

Examples

(1) If H is a subgroup and K any complex of G, prove that $HK = H$ or $KH = H$ implies that $K \subset H$.

(2) Let $D = X \cap Y$ and $M = \{X, Y\}$ where X and Y are any complexes. If Z is another complex, show that

$$X \cap Y \cap Z = D \cap Z \quad \text{and} \quad \{X, Y, Z\} = \{M, Z\}.$$

(3) If *A* and *B* are subgroups whose orders are relatively prime, prove that their intersection consists only of the unit element.

(4) Prove that if $G = HR_1 + HR_2 + \ldots + HR_n$ is a decomposition of *G* into right-hand cosets relative to a subgroup *H*, then $G = R_1^{-1}H + R_2^{-1}H + \ldots + R_n^{-1}H$ is a decomposition into left-hand cosets.

(5) Find all subgroups of order 4 of the dihedral group of order 8 (Table 11).

(6) Show that the group of Table 1 (p. 12) may be defined by the relations $C^2 = D^2 = (CD)^3 = I$.

(7) Prove that there are only two non-commutative groups of order 12 which contain an element of order 6, and that they are defined by the relations

(i) $A^6 = B^2 = (AB)^2 = I$ and   (ii) $A^6 = I, B^2 = (AB)^2 = A^3$

respectively.

(8) Show that the residues prime to 21 form an Abelian group with respect to multiplication which is isomorphic with $C_6 \times C_2$.

(9) A certain group of order 16 is defined by $A^4 = B^2 = C^2 = (AB)^2 = I, AC = CA, BC = CB$. Show that $H = I + B + C + BC$ and $K = I + A^2 + C + A^2C$ form subgroups of order 4. Find a decomposition of *G* into right-hand cosets (i) relative to *H* and (ii) relative to *K*. Verify that *H* and *K* commute, and obtain the subgroup of order 8 represented by their product. Of what type is it ?

(10) Show that the group of the preceding example is the direct product of the octic group and the group $\{C\}$.

HINTS and ANSWERS. 5. $\{A\}$, $\{A^2, B\}$, $\{AB, A^3B\}$. 7. Write the elements of the group in the form $A^l, A^lB (0 \leqslant l \leqslant 5)$. $C = B^{-1}AB$ must be a power of *A* and is of the same order as *A*. Since $C = A$ is excluded, it follows that $C = A^{-1}$. Again, we must have $B^2 = A^l$ for suitable *l* and hence $B^2 = B^{-1}B^2B = B^{-1}A^lB = A^{-l}$. Deduce that either $l = 0$ or $l = 3$.   9. $C_2 \times C_2 \times C_2$.

CHAPTER III

GROUPS OF PERMUTATIONS

19. The Symmetric Group P_n. The operation of re-arranging n distinct objects amongst themselves is called a **permutation of degree n**. The objects will be denoted by letters or simply by the numerals

$$1, 2, \ldots, n. \qquad \cdot \quad \cdot \quad \cdot \quad (3.1)$$

If the permutation A replaces 1 by a_1, 2 by a_2, ..., n by a_n, where

$$a_1, a_2, \ldots, a_n \qquad \cdot \quad \cdot \quad \cdot \quad (3.2)$$

are the numbers (3.1) in some order, we shall write

$$A = \left(\begin{array}{c} 1 \ 2 \ \ldots n \\ a_1 \, a_2 \ldots a_n \end{array} \right) \quad \cdot \qquad \cdot \qquad \cdot \quad (3.3)$$

to indicate that each number in the first row is to be replaced by the number immediately below it in the second row.

There are as many different permutations of n objects as there are arrangements * of the type (3.2).

From elementary Algebra it is known that this number is equal to $n!$

Since it is immaterial in what order the information about the n objects is given, we may rearrange the columns of the symbol (3.3) at will; indeed it is always possible to modify the expression for A in such a way that the first row consists of the numbers 1, 2, ..., n in any preassigned

---

* We use the word "arrangement" to denote the *sequence* of numbers (3.2), reserving the term "permutation" for the *operation* which replaces (3.1) by (3.2).

order, provided that the same pairs are kept in vertical alignment as in (3.3). Thus each of the $n!$ permutations can be written in $n!$ different forms. E.g.

$$\begin{pmatrix} 1 & 2 & 3 & 4 \\ 2 & 3 & 1 & 4 \end{pmatrix} = \begin{pmatrix} 2 & 1 & 4 & 3 \\ 3 & 2 & 4 & 1 \end{pmatrix} = \begin{pmatrix} 4 & 2 & 1 & 3 \\ 4 & 3 & 2 & 1 \end{pmatrix} = \cdots$$

By the *product* AB we mean the permutation obtained by first carrying out A and then * B. Suppose that

$$B = \begin{pmatrix} 1 & 2 & \dots & n \\ b_1 & b_2 & \dots & b_n \end{pmatrix} = \begin{pmatrix} a_1 & a_2 & \dots & a_n \\ c_1 & c_2 & \dots & c_n \end{pmatrix}, \quad (3.4)$$

where the second symbol for B has been derived from the first by rearranging the columns until the first row becomes identical with the second row in the symbol (3.3) for A. This has been done to prepare B for premultiplication by A. We now have

$$AB = \begin{pmatrix} 1 & 2 & \dots & n \\ a_1 & a_2 & \dots & a_n \end{pmatrix} \begin{pmatrix} a_1 & a_2 & \dots & a_n \\ c_1 & c_2 & \dots & c_n \end{pmatrix}$$
$$= \begin{pmatrix} 1 & 2 & \dots & n \\ c_1 & c_2 & \dots & c_n \end{pmatrix}; \quad (3.5)$$

for a typical number i is changed by A into a_i, and B changes a_i into c_i; hence the combined effect of A and B (in this sequence) is to change i into c_i, which agrees with the final symbol in (3.5). Notice that when the second factor B has been prepared for multiplication by A, the product AB is found simply by placing the second row of B below the first row of A. E.g., if

$$A = \begin{pmatrix} 1 & 2 & 3 & 4 \\ 2 & 3 & 4 & 1 \end{pmatrix} \quad \text{and} \quad B = \begin{pmatrix} 1 & 2 & 3 & 4 \\ 3 & 1 & 2 & 4 \end{pmatrix},$$
$$AB = \begin{pmatrix} 1 & 2 & 3 & 4 \\ 2 & 3 & 4 & 1 \end{pmatrix} \begin{pmatrix} 2 & 3 & 4 & 1 \\ 1 & 2 & 4 & 3 \end{pmatrix} = \begin{pmatrix} 1 & 2 & 3 & 4 \\ 1 & 2 & 4 & 3 \end{pmatrix}.$$

On the other hand,

$$BA = \begin{pmatrix} 1 & 2 & 3 & 4 \\ 3 & 1 & 2 & 4 \end{pmatrix} \begin{pmatrix} 3 & 1 & 2 & 4 \\ 4 & 2 & 3 & 1 \end{pmatrix} = \begin{pmatrix} 1 & 2 & 3 & 4 \\ 4 & 2 & 3 & 1 \end{pmatrix},$$

* Some authors adhere to the opposite convention.

which shows that multiplication of permutations is, in general, *not* commutative.

With a little practice the reader will become accustomed to evaluate products without having to write out the intermediate stage of preparation. Thus in the example we have just considered the product BA may be found as follows : 1 is moved to 3 by B, and 3 is moved to 4 by A ; hence by combining these operations we see that BA moves 1 to 4. Next, 2 is moved to 1 by B, and 1 is moved to 2 by A ; hence 2 is moved to 2 (is left unaltered) by BA, and so on. Having defined the multiplication of permutations, we shall now prove

THEOREM 1. *The set of all permutations of* n *objects forms a group* P_n *of order* n! ; *it is called the* **symmetric group** *of degree* n.

Proof. We shall verify postulates (I) to (IV) of Chapter I, pp. 2-3.

(i) The *closure* of the set P_n of all permutations of n objects follows immediately from the definition of multiplication.

(ii) To prove the *associative law* let us contract the symbol for permutations and write

$$A = \begin{pmatrix} \alpha \\ \beta \end{pmatrix},$$

where α is a typical representative of the numbers 1, 2, ..., n and β is its image under the operation A. Similarly, we may assume that, after being suitably prepared, two further permutations may be represented by

$$B = \begin{pmatrix} \beta \\ \gamma \end{pmatrix}, \quad C = \begin{pmatrix} \gamma \\ \delta \end{pmatrix}.$$

We then have

$$(AB)C = \left[\begin{pmatrix} \alpha \\ \beta \end{pmatrix} \begin{pmatrix} \beta \\ \gamma \end{pmatrix} \right] \begin{pmatrix} \gamma \\ \delta \end{pmatrix} = \begin{pmatrix} \alpha \\ \gamma \end{pmatrix} \begin{pmatrix} \gamma \\ \delta \end{pmatrix} = \begin{pmatrix} \alpha \\ \delta \end{pmatrix}$$

and

$$A(BC) = \begin{pmatrix} \alpha \\ \beta \end{pmatrix} \left[\begin{pmatrix} \beta \\ \gamma \end{pmatrix} \begin{pmatrix} \gamma \\ \delta \end{pmatrix} \right] = \begin{pmatrix} \alpha \\ \beta \end{pmatrix} \begin{pmatrix} \beta \\ \delta \end{pmatrix} = \begin{pmatrix} \alpha \\ \delta \end{pmatrix},$$

i.e. $$(AB)C = A(BC).$$

(iii) The *unit element* of P_n is the " identical " permutation

$$I = \begin{pmatrix} 1 & 2 & \ldots & n \\ 1 & 2 & \ldots & n \end{pmatrix} = \ldots = \begin{pmatrix} a_1 & a_2 & \ldots & a_n \\ a_1 & a_2 & \ldots & a_n \end{pmatrix},$$

which leaves each object unchanged.

(iv) If

$$A = \begin{pmatrix} 1 & 2 & \ldots & n \\ a_1 & a_2 & \ldots & a_n \end{pmatrix},$$

the *inverse* permutation may be represented by

$$A^{-1} = \begin{pmatrix} a_1 & a_2 & \ldots & a_n \\ 1 & 2 & \ldots & n \end{pmatrix}.$$

Indeed, in contracted notation, we have

$$AA^{-1} = \begin{pmatrix} \lambda \\ a_\lambda \end{pmatrix} \begin{pmatrix} a_\lambda \\ \lambda \end{pmatrix} = \begin{pmatrix} \lambda \\ \lambda \end{pmatrix} = I$$

and

$$A^{-1}A = \begin{pmatrix} a_\lambda \\ \lambda \end{pmatrix} \begin{pmatrix} \lambda \\ a_\lambda \end{pmatrix} = \begin{pmatrix} a_\lambda \\ a_\lambda \end{pmatrix} = I.$$

This concludes the proof of the theorem.

Suppose the objects $1, 2, \ldots, n$ have been separated into two mutually exclusive sets, say

$$\alpha_1, \alpha_2, \ldots, \alpha_\nu ; \quad \beta_1, \beta_2, \ldots, \beta_{n-\nu}.$$

If A permutes only the α's amongst themselves and if B operates only on the β's, then the order in which A and B are carried out is evidently irrelevant, since neither operation has an influence on the other. Hence *two permutations which operate on mutually exclusive sets of objects always commute.* E.g., if

$$A = \begin{pmatrix} 1 & 2 & 3 & 4 \\ 2 & 1 & 3 & 4 \end{pmatrix} \quad \text{and} \quad B = \begin{pmatrix} 1 & 2 & 3 & 4 \\ 1 & 2 & 4 & 3 \end{pmatrix},$$

$$AB = BA = \begin{pmatrix} 1 & 2 & 3 & 4 \\ 2 & 1 & 4 & 3 \end{pmatrix},$$

since A operates only on 1, 2 and B only on 3, 4.

20. Circular Permutations (Cycles). A permutation which interchanges m objects cyclically is called a **circular permutation** or **cycle of degree** m. Thus if m objects are denoted by 1, 2, ..., m, such a permutation is represented by

$$C = \begin{pmatrix} 1 & 2 & \ldots & m-1 & m \\ 2 & 3 & \ldots & m & 1 \end{pmatrix}. \qquad . \qquad . \qquad (3.6)$$

If we visualize the m objects arranged at m places on the circumference of a circle, the permutation C moves each object to the next place so that the last object comes to occupy the place of the first.

On account of their great importance for the theory of permutations, cycles are usually written in contracted notation thus

$$C = (1 \ 2 \ \ldots \ m),$$

indicating that each number in the bracket is to be replaced by its successor on the right, and the last number by the first. Since it is immaterial with which number we begin, we have

$$(1 \ 2 \ \ldots \ m) = (2 \ 3 \ \ldots \ m \ 1)$$
$$= (3 \ 4 \ \ldots \ m \ 1 \ 2) = (m \ 1 \ \ldots \ m-1). \qquad (3.7)$$

We shall now prove

THEOREM 2. *Every permutation can be uniquely resolved into cycles which operate on mutually exclusive sets of objects.*

Proof. Let A be a given permutation of 1, 2, ..., n. Beginning with any one of these integers, say λ, let us suppose that A moves λ to λ', λ' to λ'', λ'' to λ''', and so on ; as there are only n numbers involved in A, there must be an index r, where $1 \leqslant r \leqslant n$ such that

$$\lambda^{(r)} = \lambda.$$

Thus some part of the effect of A is equivalent to the cycle

$$L = (\lambda \; \lambda' \; \lambda'' \; \ldots \; \lambda^{(r-1)}). \qquad . \qquad . \qquad (3.8)$$

If $r = n$, all numbers have been accounted for and we have $A = L$. On the other hand, if $r < n$, let μ be a number not contained in L and suppose that A carries μ into μ', μ' into μ'', and so on until we return to μ, as we must do after at most $n - r$ steps ; for the images of μ and its successors are certainly different from the λ's, or else two numbers, one μ and one λ, would have the same image. We have therefore isolated another cycle

$$M = (\mu \; \mu' \; \mu'' \; \ldots \; \mu^{(s-1)}),$$

say. If $r + s = n$ we have proved that $A = LM = ML$ (see the remark at the end of § 19, p. 65).

On the other hand, if $r + s < n$, the process may be continued, and more cycles are extracted from A until finally each of the n objects has been drawn into one of the cycles. Thus we get a decomposition of A :

$$A = (\lambda \, \lambda' \ldots \lambda^{(r-1)})(\mu \, \mu' \ldots \mu^{(s-1)}) \ldots (\rho \, \rho' \ldots \rho^{(u-1)}), \quad (3.9)$$

where

$$r + s + \ldots + u = n. \qquad . \qquad . \qquad (3.10)$$

This resolution into mutually exclusive cycles is *unique*, save for the order in which the cycles occur (we have already seen that they all commute), and save for the alternative ways in which each cycle may be expressed (see 3.7) ; for it is clear that two essentially different products of cycles correspond to different permutations.

Example :

$$\begin{pmatrix} 1 & 2 & 3 & 4 & 5 & 6 & 7 & 8 \\ 4 & 5 & 2 & 8 & 3 & 6 & 1 & 7 \end{pmatrix} = (1 \; 4 \; 8 \; 7)(2 \; 5 \; 3)(6).$$

F

A cycle which consists of a single letter merely indicates that this letter is unaltered ; such cycles are often omitted from the resolution of a given permutation into cycles, thus

$$\begin{pmatrix} 1 & 2 & 3 & 4 & 5 & 6 & 7 \\ 4 & 7 & 3 & 5 & 1 & 6 & 2 \end{pmatrix} = (1 \ 4 \ 5)(2 \ 7)$$

it being understood that 3 and 6 remain fixed.*

Thus $(1 \ 2 \ 3) = \begin{pmatrix} 1 & 2 & 3 \\ 2 & 3 & 1 \end{pmatrix}$, when $n = 3$,

$(1 \ 2 \ 3) = \begin{pmatrix} 1 & 2 & 3 & 4 & 5 \\ 2 & 3 & 1 & 4 & 5 \end{pmatrix}$, when $n = 5$.

It is easy to write down the powers of a given cycle

$$C = (1 \ 2 \ \dots \ m).$$

Since C moves every letter to the next place on the circumference of a circle, C^2 sends every letter two places along, C^3 three places along, and so on.   Generally, C^k replaces x by $x + k$ where this number has to be reduced to its least positive remainder relative to m.   In particular, it follows that C is of order m, i.e.

$$(1 \ 2 \ \dots \ m)^m = I, \quad . \quad . \quad . \quad (3.11)$$

because C^m replaces x by $x + m$, which is equivalent to x. *Thus a cycle of degree* m *is of order* m.   E.g., when $m = 6$, we have

$$(1 \ 2 \ 3 \ 4 \ 5 \ 6)^2 = (1 \ 3 \ 5)(2 \ 4 \ 6)$$
$$(1 \ 2 \ 3 \ 4 \ 5 \ 6)^3 = (1 \ 4)(2 \ 5)(3 \ 6)$$
$$(1 \ 2 \ 3 \ 4 \ 5 \ 6)^4 = (1 \ 5 \ 3)(2 \ 6 \ 4)$$
$$(1 \ 2 \ 3 \ 4 \ 5 \ 6)^5 = (1 \ 6 \ 5 \ 4 \ 3 \ 2)$$
$$(1 \ 2 \ 3 \ 4 \ 5 \ 6)^6 = I.$$

Let

$$P = C_1 C_2 \dots C_r \quad . \quad . \quad . \quad (3.12)$$

* The identical permutation I is then usually written (1) to save it from total evanescence.

be the resolution of a given permutation into mutually exclusive cycles of orders

$$\mu_1, \mu_2, \ldots, \mu_r . \quad . \quad . \quad . \quad (3.13)$$

respectively. Since these cycles commute we have (see (1.7))

$$P^m = C_1{}^m C_2{}^m \ldots C_r{}^m.$$

Suppose now that P is of order m so that

$$C_1{}^m C_2{}^m \ldots C_r{}^m = I, \quad . \quad . \quad . \quad (3.14)$$

and therefore

$$C_1{}^m = (C_2 C_3 \ldots C_r)^{-m}.$$

Now $C_2, C_3, \ldots, C_r$ do not permute the letters which are involved in C_1. Hence $C_1{}^m = I$. Similarly, we prove that $C_2{}^m = C_3{}^m = \ldots = C_r{}^m = I$. It follows that m is a multiple of each of the integers (3.13). Conversely, if m is any such multiple, (3.14) is fulfilled. Thus *the order of any permutation is the* L.C.M. *of the orders of its component (mutually exclusive) cycles.*

A permutation is said to be **regular** if all its cycles are of the same degree.

As an example we give a list of the six permutations of P_3 ($n = 3$), each resolved into cycles :

$$I = (1), \quad A = (1 \ 2 \ 3), \quad B = (1 \ 3 \ 2),$$
$$C = (1 \ 2), \quad D = (1 \ 3), \quad E = (2 \ 3).$$

We have

$$A^3 = (1 \ 2 \ 3)^3 = I, \quad C^2 = (1 \ 2)^2 = I, \quad (AC)^2 = (2 \ 3)^2 = I.$$

Comparing these relations with (2.45) p. 44, we see that P_3 is isomorphic with the abstract group of Table 1, see p. 12. Thus the elements of that group may be interpreted or **represented** as permutations, and all relations which follow from the multiplication table have their counterpart in relations between the permutations of the group P_3. This affords an indirect verification of the associative law for the abstract group under consideration (p. 13), because this law is known to hold for all permutations, and in particular for P_3.

21. Classes of Permutations. Two permutations, A and B of degree n, are said to be **similar** or **conjugate** * *with respect to* P_n if there exists a permutation T in P_n such that

$$B = T^{-1}AT. \qquad . \qquad . \qquad . \qquad (3.15)$$

This concept is of fundamental importance in the theory of groups and will be more fully discussed in the next chapter.

The relation between two conjugate permutations is best understood when they are resolved into cycles. Let

$$A = C_1 C_2 \ldots C_r \qquad . \qquad . \qquad . \qquad (3.16)$$

be a given permutation decomposed into r mutually exclusive cycles, and let

$$T = \left(\begin{array}{c} 1 \ 2 \ \ldots \ n \\ 1' \ 2' \ \ldots \ n' \end{array} \right) = \left(\begin{array}{c} \lambda \\ \lambda' \end{array} \right)$$

be any permutation of P_n whatsoever. We wish to find an expression for $T^{-1}AT$. Since

$$T^{-1}AT = (T^{-1}C_1 T)(T^{-1}C_2 T) \ldots (T^{-1}C_r T), \qquad (3.17)$$

it is sufficient to evaluate a typical factor

$$T^{-1}CT,$$

where

$$C = (a_1 \ a_2 \ \ldots \ a_m) = \left(\begin{array}{c} a_i \\ a_{i+1} \end{array} \right) \qquad . \qquad . \qquad (3.18)$$

is a cycle of degree m. (In the last symbol a_{m+1} must be considered identical with a_1.) Generally we can write

---

* This agrees with the terminology of Chapter IV. In a different context, some authors speak of conjugate permutations when we should use the terms '*reciprocal*' or '*inverse*' (A. C. Aitken, *Determinants and Matrices*, 4th ed., p. 33).

$$T^{-1} = \begin{pmatrix} \lambda' \\ \lambda \end{pmatrix}.$$

If λ does not occur in C, then λ' is not altered by the permutation $T^{-1}CT$, because T^{-1} transforms λ' into λ which is changed back into λ' by T, the factor C having remained passive. On the other hand, if $\lambda = a_i$, we have

$$a_i' \longrightarrow a_i \ (\text{by } T^{-1}), \quad a_i \longrightarrow a_{i+1} \ (\text{by } C),$$
$$a_{i+1} \longrightarrow a_{i+1}' \ (\text{by } T),$$

so that $T^{-1}CT$ changes a_i' into a_{i+1}'. Thus we can write

$$T^{-1}CT = (a_1' \ a_2' \ldots a_m'). \qquad . \qquad . \ (3.19)$$

On comparing (3.18) with (3.19) we observe that $\mathbf{T^{-1}CT}$ *is derived from* C *by applying the permutation* T *to the letters in the bracket representing* C. This rule holds generally for any product of cycles. E.g., if

$$A = (1\ 3)(2\ 4\ 5) \quad \text{and} \quad T = \begin{pmatrix} 1\ 2\ 3\ 4\ 5 \\ 2\ 4\ 5\ 1\ 3 \end{pmatrix}$$

we have

$$T^{-1}AT = (2\ 5)(4\ 1\ 3)$$

replacing, in the expression for A, 1 by 2, 3 by 5, ... as required by T.

Let us suppose that in (3.16) the cycles are arranged in *non-decreasing* order, including those of order 1, and let these orders be denoted by

$$1 \leqslant \mu_1 \leqslant \mu_2 \leqslant \ldots \leqslant \mu_r \leqslant n, \quad . \quad . \quad . \ (3.20)$$

where

$$\mu_1 + \mu_2 + \ldots + \mu_r = n. \quad . \quad . \quad . \ (3.21)$$

Thus every permutation of degree n is associated with a **partition** of n into positive integers, namely, the degrees of the cycles into which it is decomposed. *Two permutations which correspond to the same partition are said to belong to the same* **class** * *of* P_n. It follows from (3.16) and (3.17) that

* Not to be confused with the distinction between even and odd permutations (p. 74 below). The word '*class*' will not be used by us in this connection.

conjugate permutations belong to the same class. Conversely, if A and B are two permutations of the same class, say

$$A = (a_1 \ldots a_{\mu_1})(b_1 \ldots b_{\mu_2}) \ldots (u_1 \ldots u_{\mu_r})$$

and

$$B = (\alpha_1 \ldots \alpha_{\mu_1})(\beta_1 \ldots \beta_{\mu_2}) \ldots (\omega_1 \ldots \omega_{\mu_r}),$$

then a permutation T can be found such that

$$B = T^{-1}AT. \qquad \cdot \qquad \cdot \qquad \cdot \qquad (3.22)$$

Indeed if we put

$$T = \begin{pmatrix} a_1 \ldots a_{\mu_1} & b_1 \ldots b_{\mu_2} & \ldots & u_1 \ldots u_{\mu_r} \\ \alpha_1 \ldots \alpha_{\mu_1} & \beta_1 \ldots \beta_{\mu_2} & \ldots & \omega_1 \ldots \omega_{\mu_r} \end{pmatrix},$$

the evaluation of the product on the right-hand side of (3.22) amounts to replacing the letters in the cycles of A by the corresponding Greek letters, a process which turns A into B. Thus we have proved the important result:

THEOREM 3. *Two permutations are conjugate with respect to* P_n *if, and only if, they belong to the same class.*

There are clearly as many classes of P_n as there are different ways of partitioning n in accordance with (3.20) and (3.21). It is important to know how many permutations belong to a given class. Instead of specifying the class by a partition (3.21), let us suppose that each of its members involves

α_1 cycles of degree 1,
α_2 cycles of degree 2,
. . . .
α_n cycles of degree n,

where

$$1\alpha_1 + 2\alpha_2 + \ldots + n\alpha_n = n. \qquad \cdot \qquad \cdot \qquad (3.23)$$

The set of *non-negative* integers

$$(\alpha) : \alpha_1, \alpha_2, \ldots, \alpha_n \qquad \cdot \qquad \cdot \qquad (3.24)$$

completely determines the class (α). To construct all permutations of (α) imagine a pattern of empty brackets

$$\underbrace{(\cdot)(\cdot) \ldots (\cdot)}_{\alpha_1}\underbrace{(\cdot \cdot)(\cdot \cdot) \ldots (\cdot \cdot)}_{\alpha_2} \ldots \qquad . \quad (3.25)$$

which correspond precisely to the cycles of a typical permutation A of (α). There are altogether n blank spaces in the pattern, and these can be filled with the letters $1, 2, \ldots, n$ in $n!$ ways. However, not all these $n!$ arrangements correspond to distinct permutations. For the α_k cycles of degree k ($k = 1, 2, \ldots, n$) may be permuted in any manner without causing a change in the resulting permutation A. Thus the same permutation is obtained

$$\alpha_1! \; \alpha_2! \ldots \alpha_n! \qquad . \quad . \quad . \quad (3.26)$$

times if all $n!$ arrangements are considered. Also, it should be remembered that a cycle of degree k may be written in k different ways since each of its letters may be brought to the leading position in the bracket (p. 66). Hence α_k cycles of degree k admit of k^{α_k} equivalent arrangements. In this way each permutation has been counted

$$1^{\alpha_1}2^{\alpha_2} \ldots n^{\alpha_n} \qquad . \quad . \quad . \quad (3.27)$$

times. Thus in order to obtain the exact number h_α of permutations in the class (α), we must divide $n!$ by (3.26) and (3.27). This gives the formula

$$h_\alpha = \frac{n!}{1^{\alpha_1}\alpha_1! \; 2^{\alpha_2}\alpha_2! \ldots n^{\alpha_n}\alpha_n!} \; , \quad . \quad . \quad (3.28)$$

which is due to Cauchy.[*]

22. Transpositions. A cycle of the form (ab) is called a transposition ; it interchanges the letters a and b and leaves all the others unaltered. We note that (see (3.11))

$$(ab)^2 = I, \quad (ab) = (ab)^{-1} = (ba).$$

Let

$$x_1, x_2, \ldots, x_n$$

be independent variables and consider the *product of differences*

[*] *Exercice d'analyse et de physique mathématique*, iii (1844), p. 173.

$$\left.\begin{aligned}
\Delta = (x_1 - x_2)(x_1 - x_3)(x_1 - x_4) \ldots (x_1 - x_n) \\
\times (x_2 - x_3)(x_2 - x_4) \ldots (x_2 - x_n) \\
\times (x_3 - x_4) \ldots (x_3 - x_n) \\
\ldots \\
\times (x_{n-1} - x_n)
\end{aligned}\right\}. \quad (3.29)$$

If the variables are subjected to a permutation A, the function Δ is formally changed into a new function Δ_A which is, however, identically equal either to Δ or to $-\Delta$. We shall write

$$\Delta_A = \zeta(A)\Delta, \qquad (3.30)$$

where $\zeta(A)$ is a function of the permutation A which has the property that

$$\zeta(A) = 1 \text{ or } -1. \qquad (3.31)$$

DEFINITION 1. *A permutation* A *is said to be* **even** *or* **odd** *according as* $\zeta(A) = 1$ *or* $\zeta(A) = -1$. *The function* $\zeta(A)$ *is called the* **alternating character** *of* P_n. The most important fact about this function is expressed in the following :

THEOREM 4. *If* A *and* B *are any two permutations,*

$$\zeta(AB) = \zeta(A)\zeta(B) ; \qquad (3.32)$$

i.e. the product of two even or two odd permutations is even whilst the product of an even and an odd permutation is odd.

Proof. If we apply the permutation B to both sides of (3.30), we get

$$\Delta_{AB} = \zeta(A)\Delta_B = \zeta(A)\zeta(B)\Delta. \qquad (3.33)$$

On the other hand, if we let the permutation AB take the place of A, the identity (3.30) becomes

$$\Delta_{AB} = \zeta(AB)\Delta, \qquad (3.34)$$

whence we deduce (3.32) by comparing (3.33) and (3.34).

Evidently, if I is the identical permutation, we have $\Delta_I \equiv \Delta$, i.e.

$$\zeta(I) = 1. \qquad (3.35)$$

Hence, on putting $A = B^{-1}$ in (3.32), we find that

$$\zeta(B)\zeta(B^{-1}) = 1, \qquad . \qquad . \qquad . \qquad (3.36)$$

or in view of (3.31)

$$\zeta(B) = \zeta(B^{-1}). \qquad . \qquad . \qquad . \qquad (3.37)$$

Also, if A and B are any two permutations, we have by a repeated application of (3.32)

$$\zeta(B^{-1}AB) = \zeta(B^{-1})\zeta(A)\zeta(B) = \zeta(B^{-1})\zeta(B)\zeta(A),$$

whence by (3.36)

$$\zeta(B^{-1}AB) = \zeta(A), \qquad . \qquad . \qquad . \qquad (3.38)$$

i.e. permutations of the same class have the same alternating character.

THEOREM 5.   *All transpositions are odd permutations.*

Proof. Let $A = (12)$. The function $\Delta_{(12)}$ is obtained from Δ by an interchange of x_1 and x_2. We see by (3.29) that this changes the sign of the first factor only, all other factors being either left unaltered or simply permuted. Thus

$$\Delta_{(12)} = -\Delta,$$

i.e.

$$\zeta((12)) = -1.$$

To obtain the alternating character of other transpositions we use the identities

$$(1a) = (2a)(12)(2a)^{-1}, \quad (a > 2), \qquad . \qquad . \qquad (3.39)$$

$$(ab) = (1b)(1a)(1b)^{-1}, \quad (1 < a < b), . \qquad . \qquad (3.40)$$

whence by (3.38)

$$\zeta((ab)) = \zeta((1a)) = \zeta((12)),$$

and therefore

$$\zeta((ab)) = -1$$

for all transpositions.

THEOREM 6.   *Every permutation can, in infinitely many ways, be expressed as a product of transpositions, the number of transpositions in such a product being always even or always odd according as the given permutation is even or odd.*

Proof. We shall first show that every cycle can be expressed as a product of transpositions ; indeed

$$(a_1 a_2 \ldots a_m) = (a_1 a_2)(a_1 a_3) \ldots (a_1 a_m), \quad . \quad (3.41)$$

as can be verified by evaluating the product on the right-hand side : $a_1 \longrightarrow a_2, a_2 \longrightarrow a_1 \longrightarrow a_3, a_3 \longrightarrow a_1 \longrightarrow a_4$, and so on.

Since every permutation can be written as a product of cycles, the first part of the theorem is proved. As the transpositions in (3.41) have a letter in common, they do not, in general, commute. Also, the product is not changed by the insertion of pairs of factors such as

$$(ab)(ab),$$

which are equivalent to the identical permutation. For this reason alone the factorization into transpositions cannot be unique.

Suppose that a given permutation A is expressed as a product of transpositions in any way whatever,

$$A = T_1 T_2 \ldots T_s. \quad . \quad . \quad (3.42)$$

By Theorems 4 and 5 we have

$$\zeta(A) = \prod_{i=1}^{s} \zeta(T_i) = (-1)^s.$$

Hence the number of factors in (3.42) is even or odd according as A is even or odd.

We see from (3.40) that every transposition can be expressed in terms of the special transpositions $(1k)$, where $k = 2, 3, \ldots, n$. Using the technical term introduced in Chapter II, p. 42, we may enunciate

THEOREM 7. *The symmetric group P_n may be generated by the $n - 1$ transpositions*

$$(12), (13), \ldots, (1n). \quad . \quad . \quad (3.43)$$

23. The Alternating Group A_n. We return to the distinction between even and odd permutations introduced on p. 74.

THEOREM 8. *In any group of permutations G either all or exactly half the permutations are even. The even permutations of G form a group by themselves.*

Proof. If G contains no odd permutation, there is nothing to prove. Suppose that Q is an odd permutation belonging to G so that $\zeta(Q) = -1$. As X runs through the whole group, so does QX where Q is fixed (p. 32). Hence

$$\sum_X \zeta(X) = \sum_X \zeta(QX).$$

On the other hand,

$$\sum \zeta(QX) = \sum \zeta(Q)\zeta(X) = -\sum \zeta(X),$$

whence

$$\sum \zeta(X) = 0.$$

This means that the sum contains an equal number of positive and negative terms, i.e. there are as many even as odd permutations in G. Also, it is evident from Theorem 4 that the even permutations of G obey the postulate of closure and therefore form a (proper or improper) subgroup of G.

Special interest is attached to the case in which G is the symmetric group P_n.

DEFINITION 2. *The set of all even permutations of degree n forms a group* A_n *of order* $\frac{1}{2}n!$, *which is called the* **alternating group** *of degree* n.

E.g., the alternating group A_4 is of order $\frac{1}{2}(4!)$, i.e. 12, and consists of the following permutations (arranged according to classes of P_4):

$$(1) \ (=I)$$
$$A_4 : \ (1\ 2)(3\ 4), \quad (1\ 3)(2\ 4), \quad (1\ 4)(2\ 3)$$
$$(1\ 2\ 3), \quad (1\ 2\ 4), \quad (1\ 3\ 2), \quad (1\ 3\ 4), \quad (1\ 4\ 2),$$
$$(1\ 4\ 3), \quad (2\ 3\ 4), \quad (2\ 4\ 3).$$

A permutation is even if, and only if, it can be written as the product of an even number of transpositions. By Theorem 7 these transpositions may be selected from the set (3.43) and then arranged in pairs. Since

$$(1i)(1j) = (1ij) = (12j)(12i)(12j)^2,$$

provided that $i \neq j$, $i > 1$, $j > 1$, we have

THEOREM 9. *The alternating group* A_n *may be generated by the* $n - 2$ *ternary cycles*

$$(1\ 2\ 3), (1\ 2\ 4), \ldots, (1\ 2\ n). \qquad . \qquad . \quad (3.44)$$

24. Cayley's Theorem. It was not until comparatively late that the abstract concept of a group was fully appreciated. The earlier literature on the subject, including the classical works of Cauchy, Galois and Jordan,* dealt exclusively with groups of permutations, although they contain many results which apply equally well to all finite groups. A close study of permutation groups is, however, of more than historical interest, because we shall presently show that every finite group whatsoever is isomorphic with a suitable group of permutations. This important fact was discovered by A. Cayley.†

Let

$$\mathbf{G} : G_1, G_2, \ldots, G_g \qquad . \qquad . \qquad . \quad (3.45)$$

be an abstract group of order g. If P is any one of these elements, the products

$$G_1 P, G_2 P, \ldots, G_g P \qquad . \qquad . \qquad . \quad (3.46)$$

are g distinct elements of $\mathbf{G}$ and therefore represent a rearrangement of (3.45). Thus with every element P of $\mathbf{G}$ we can associate a permutation of degree g, namely

$$P' = \begin{pmatrix} G_1 & G_2 & \ldots & G_g \\ G_1 P & G_2 P & \ldots & G_g P \end{pmatrix}. \qquad . \qquad . \quad (3.47)$$

---

* C. Jordan, *Traité des substitutions*, Paris, 1870.
† *Phil. Mag.* vol. vii (4), 1854, pp. 40-47.

The objects on which this permutation operates are the group elements themselves. It is convenient to use the abbreviated notation

$$P' = \begin{pmatrix} G_i \\ G_i P \end{pmatrix} \quad (i = 1, 2, \ldots, g). \quad . \quad . \quad (3.48)$$

When G_i runs through the whole group, so does $G_i X$ where X is a fixed element of G. The information contained in (3.48) may therefore also be expressed by

$$P' = \begin{pmatrix} G_i X \\ G_i X P \end{pmatrix}. \quad . \quad . \quad . \quad (3.49)$$

Similarly, let

$$Q' = \begin{pmatrix} G_i \\ G_i Q \end{pmatrix} \quad . \quad . \quad . \quad (3.50)$$

be the permutation corresponding to the element Q. If P and Q are distinct, the permutations (3.48) and (3.50) are certainly not equal ; indeed, since $G_i P \neq G_i Q$, they have a different effect on each of the permuted objects. Hence we have established a *(1, 1)-correspondence* between the elements $P, Q, \ldots$ of G and the set (3.48) of permutations $P', Q', \ldots$.

Next, let us evaluate the product $P'Q'$; we find that

$$P'Q' = \begin{pmatrix} G_i \\ G_i P \end{pmatrix}\begin{pmatrix} G_i \\ G_i Q \end{pmatrix} = \begin{pmatrix} G_i \\ G_i P \end{pmatrix}\begin{pmatrix} G_i P \\ G_i P Q \end{pmatrix} = \begin{pmatrix} G_i \\ G_i P Q \end{pmatrix}.$$

The result is the permutation which corresponds to the group element PQ ; i.e. we have

$$(PQ)' = P'Q'. \quad . \quad . \quad . \quad (3.51)$$

Thus we have shown that the correspondence

$$P \longleftrightarrow P'$$

is in fact an *isomorphism*. The set of permutations of degree g

$$\mathsf{G}' : P', Q', \ldots$$

forms a group (a subgroup of P_g) which possesses the same structure as the given abstract group G.

The permutation which corresponds to I is evidently the identical permutation

$$I' = \begin{pmatrix} G_i \\ G_i I \end{pmatrix} = \begin{pmatrix} G_i \\ G_i \end{pmatrix}.$$

Any other permutation of G' displaces each group element since it changes G_i into $G_i P$, which differs from G_i unless $P = I$.

We shall now resolve P' into cycles. Let the corresponding abstract element be of order r, thus

$$P^r = I. \qquad . \qquad . \qquad . \qquad (3.52)$$

Beginning with any element G of G, we know that it is changed by P' into GP, which in turn is changed into GP^2; the image of GP^2 under P' is GP^3, and so on until we come to GP^{r-1} which is transformed into GP^r, i.e. into G, in virtue of (3.52). Thus we see that P' contains the cycle

$$(G, GP, GP^2, \ldots, GP^{r-1}) \qquad . \qquad . \qquad (3.53)$$

of order r. If H is an element of G not included in (3.53), we can isolate a further cycle of P', namely

$$(H, HP, HP^2, \ldots, HP^{r-1}),$$

which is likewise of order r. This process is to be continued until all elements of G have been accounted for. We have then arrived at the resolution

$$P' = (G, GP, \ldots, GP^{r-1})(H, HP, \ldots, HP^{r-1}) \ldots$$
$$(L, LP, \ldots, LP^{r-1}),$$

which shows that P' is a *regular* permutation (p. 69).

We may summarize our results as follows:

THEOREM 10 (Cayley). *With each element* P *of an abstract group*

$$G: G_1, G_2, \ldots, G_g,$$

we can associate a regular permutation

$$P' = \begin{pmatrix} G_1 & G_2 & \ldots & G_g \\ G_1 P & G_2 P & \ldots & G_g P \end{pmatrix}.$$

The set of all these permutations forms a group G' *(subgroup of* P_g*) which is isomorphic with* G*; i.e. if* $P \longleftrightarrow P'$ *and* $Q \longleftrightarrow Q'$*, then* $PQ \longleftrightarrow P'Q'$*.*

When an abstract group G is isomorphic with a group G' whose elements are concrete mathematical entities such as permutations or matrices, we say that G' is a **faithful representation** of G in terms of permutations or matrices, as the case may be. All properties of G are also possessed by G'. Conversely, any information about G' which does not really depend on the special nature of its elements, applies equally to G. The idea of representing an abstract group by concrete elements is in some respects analogous to the use of co-ordinates in the treatment of geometrical problems ; it carries with it certain analytical advantages but violates the principle of purity of method.

The permutation group G' which, according to Cayley's Theorem, may be associated with an abstract group G is called the **regular representation** of G.

It is quite possible for an abstract group to admit of more than one faithful representation in terms of permutations which may even be of different degrees. E.g., consider the group

$$G : I, A, B, C, D, E \quad . \quad . \quad . \quad (3.54)$$

of Table 1 (p. 12). To obtain its regular representation we postmultiply the set by each of the elements in turn, thereby transforming it into the various columns of the multiplication table. In this way the regular permutations can immediately be written down, namely

$$I' = \begin{pmatrix} I & A & B & C & D & E \\ I & A & B & C & D & E \end{pmatrix} = (I)(A)(B)(C)(D)(E)$$

$$A' = \begin{pmatrix} I & A & B & C & D & E \\ A & B & I & D & E & C \end{pmatrix} = (I\ A\ B)(C\ D\ E)$$

$$B' = \begin{pmatrix} I & A & B & C & D & E \\ B & I & A & E & C & D \end{pmatrix} = (I\ B\ A)(C\ E\ D)$$

$$C' = \begin{pmatrix} I & A & B & C & D & E \\ C & E & D & I & B & A \end{pmatrix} = (I\ C)(A\ E)(B\ D)$$

$$D' = \begin{pmatrix} I & A & B & C & D & E \\ D & C & E & A & I & B \end{pmatrix} = (I\ D)(A\ C)(B\ E)$$

$$E' = \begin{pmatrix} I & A & B & C & D & E \\ E & D & C & B & A & I \end{pmatrix} = (I\ E)(A\ D)(B\ C).$$

On the other hand, as we have seen on p. 69, the same group may be faithfully represented by the six permutations of P_3, which operates only on three symbols.

25. Transitive Groups. In this and the following section we shall consider permutations of a fixed degree n, i.e. we shall be concerned with subgroups G of the symmetric group P_n. The objects on which G operates will again be denoted by $1, 2, \ldots, n$ or by letters $\alpha, \beta, \ldots$.

DEFINITION 3. *A group of permutations is said to be* **transitive** *if it contains at least one permutation which transforms any one of the* n *letters into any other letter. Otherwise the group is said to be* **intransitive**.

Note that this concept applies to groups of permutations only.

Let a permutation which changes α into β be denoted by $P_{\alpha\beta}$ irrespective of the effect it has on the remaining letters. We note that $P_{\alpha\beta}^{-1}$ changes β into α. There may of course be more than one such permutation for a given pair α, β.

Evidently the symmetric group P_n is transitive, as it contains all possible permutations, including the transposition $(\alpha\beta)$ which transforms α into β.

On the other hand, the group

$$V_1 : \quad (1), \quad (1\ 2), \quad (3\ 4), \quad (1\ 2)(3\ 4)$$

of order and degree 4 is intransitive because none of its permutations changes 1 into 3. Incidentally, this group is isomorphic with the group

$$V_2 : \quad (1), \quad (1\ 2)(3\ 4), \quad (1\ 3)(2\ 4), \quad (1\ 4)(2\ 3)$$

which, on the contrary, is transitive. Both groups are isomorphic with the four-group ((2.52), p. 49).

The set of permutations of G which leave the first symbol (1) unaltered forms a subgroup G_1 ; for the identical permutation certainly belongs to this set, as does the product of any two of its members. Generally, we denote by G_α the subgroup of all permutations of G which leave the letter α unaltered.

THEOREM 11. *A group of permutations G of degree* n *is transitive if, and only if, the subgroup G_1 is of index* n *relative to G.*

Proof. (i) Suppose that G is transitive. By hypothesis it contains permutations

$$P_{11}, P_{12}, \ldots, P_{1n} \qquad \cdot \qquad \cdot \qquad \cdot \quad (3.55)$$

which transform 1 into 1, 2, . . ., n respectively. We shall prove that the n complexes

$$G_1 P_{11}, G_1 P_{12}, \ldots, G_1 P_{1n} . \qquad \cdot \qquad \cdot \quad (3.56)$$

are in fact a complete system of cosets of G relative to G_1. The complexes (3.56) are distinct because the letter 1 is transformed differently by permutations belonging to different complexes. For let Q be any permutation of G whatsoever and suppose that Q changes 1 into α, say. Since $P_{1\alpha}^{-1}$ changes α back into 1, the permutation $QP_{1\alpha}^{-1}$ leaves 1 invariant and accordingly belongs to G_1, thus

$$QP_{1\alpha}^{-1} \subset G_1, \quad Q \subset G_1 P_{1\alpha}.$$

Hence the complexes (3.56) comprise the whole group, i.e. G_1 is of index n.

(ii) Conversely, if G_1 is of index n, let

$$G = G_1 R_1 + G_1 R_2 + \ldots + G_1 R_n$$

be the decomposition of G into cosets relative to G_1. It is easy to see that no two of the permutations

$$R_1, R_2, \ldots, R_n . \qquad \cdot \qquad \cdot \quad (.3.57)$$

G

transform 1 into the same symbol ; for if R_i and R_j were to change 1 into the same letter α, the permutation $R_iR_j^{-1}$ would leave 1 unaltered and would therefore belong to G_1. By Chapter II, Lemma 2 (p. 34), this would imply that $G_1R_i = G_1R_j$, which is impossible. Hence the permutations (3.57) may in some order be taken for the permutations (3.55) whose existence has thus been established.

Finally, if α and β are any two of the n letters of G, the permutation $P_{1\alpha}^{-1}P_{1\beta}$ transforms α into β because the first factor changes α into 1 and the second 1 into β. Hence G is transitive.

Since the order of a group is divisible by the index of any of its subgroups (p. 37), we have the

COROLLARY. *The order of a transitive group of permutations of degree* n *is divisible by* n.

The concept of transitiveness may be generalized in the following way.

DEFINITION 4. *A group of permutations is said to be* **k-ply transitive** *if it contains at least one permutation which changes any set of* k *distinct symbols* $\alpha_1, \alpha_2, \ldots, \alpha_k$ *into any other such set* $\beta_1, \beta_2, \ldots \beta_k$ *(the α's need not be distinct from the β's). A* k-*ply transitive group is a fortiori* l-*ply transitive, where* $l < k$.

The symmetric group P_n is obviously k-ply transitive, where k is any of the integers $1, 2, \ldots, n$.

The number of distinct sets of symbols $\alpha_1, \alpha_2, \ldots, \alpha_k$ is

$$v = n(n-1)\ldots(n-k+1),$$

regard being had to the order of the symbols in the set. Let H be the subgroup of all permutations of G which leave the set

$$1, 2, 3, \ldots, k$$

unchanged. By arguments which are analogous to those used in the proof of Theorem 11 it can be shown that the index of H relative to G is equal to v, there being one coset corresponding to each of the v sets of k letters. Hence we have the result:

THEOREM 12. *The order of a* k-*ply transitive group of degree* n *is divisible by* $n(n-1)\ldots(n-k+1)$.

Alternatively we might have developed the concept of multiple transitiveness inductively by using as definition what from our point of view is a criterion.

THEOREM 13. *The group* G *is* k-*ply transitive if* (i) G *is simply transitive and* (ii) G_1 *is* (k-1)-*ply transitive with regard to the symbols* 2, 3, ..., n. E.g., the group $G \equiv A_4$ on p. 77 is doubly transitive because the group G_1, which consists of the permutations

$$I, \quad (2\ 3\ 4), \quad (2\ 4\ 3),$$

is evidently simply transitive, as its leading symbol (2) is capable of being transformed into each of the remaining symbols (3 and 4).

26. Primitive Groups. Let G be a *transitive* group and suppose that it is possible to arrange the n letters on which it operates in an array of r rows and s columns, where

$$rs = n, \quad r > 1, \quad s > 1, \quad . \quad . \quad . \quad (3.58)$$

thus

$$\left.\begin{array}{l} a_1, a_2, \ldots, a_s \\ b_1, b_2, \ldots, b_s \\ \cdots\cdots\cdots\cdots \\ k_1, k_2, \ldots, k_s \end{array}\right\} (r \text{ rows}), \quad . \quad . \quad . \quad (3.59)$$

in such a way that the permutations of G either permute the letters of any one row amongst themselves or else interchange the letters of one row with those of another row (in some order) so that two letters which stand in different rows of (3.59) are never transformed into letters of the same row and vice versa. A transitive group which has this property is said to be **imprimitive**, and the rows of (3.59) are called **imprimitive systems**. A group for which no imprimitive systems can be found is said to be **primitive**. It should be noted that this distinction applies to transitive permutation groups only.

Example 1. The group $G = \{(1\ 2\ 3\ 4)\}$ which consists of the permutations

$$I, \quad (1\ 2\ 3\ 4), \quad (1\ 3)(2\ 4), \quad (1\ 4\ 3\ 2),$$

is imprimitive, having the imprimitive system

$$\left.\begin{array}{cc} 1 & 3 \\ 2 & 4 \end{array}\right|,$$

which, by the four permutations of G, is changed into

$$\left.\begin{array}{cc} 1 & 3 \\ 2 & 4 \end{array}\right|, \quad \left.\begin{array}{cc} 2 & 4 \\ 3 & 1 \end{array}\right|, \quad \left.\begin{array}{cc} 3 & 1 \\ 4 & 2 \end{array}\right|, \quad \left.\begin{array}{cc} 4 & 2 \\ 1 & 3 \end{array}\right|$$

respectively.

Example 2. It is quite possible that one group may possess several sets of imprimitive systems. Thus in the case of the four-group

$$(1), \quad (1\ 2)(3\ 4), \quad (1\ 3)(2\ 4), \quad (1\ 4)(2\ 3),$$

each of the arrays

$$\left.\begin{array}{cc} 1 & 2 \\ 3 & 4 \end{array}\right|, \quad \left.\begin{array}{cc} 1 & 3 \\ 2 & 4 \end{array}\right|, \quad \left.\begin{array}{cc} 1 & 4 \\ 2 & 3 \end{array}\right|$$

can serve as a set of imprimitive systems.

A *doubly-transitive* group is always *primitive*. For if the rows of the array

$$\begin{array}{l} a_1,\ a_2,\ \ldots \\ b_1,\ b_2,\ \ldots \\ \cdots\cdots\cdots \end{array}$$

were imprimitive systems, the group could not contain a permutation that transforms the pair a_1, a_2 into a_1, b_2, which would be a contradiction to the definition of double transitiveness.

In particular, all symmetric groups P_n are primitive.

27. General Remarks about Transformations. Let Γ be an aggregate of objects x, y, ... (Their nature need not be further specified at present.) By a **mapping** of Γ into itself we mean an operation A that associates with every x a *unique* image x^A *which is itself an element of* Γ ; we shall use the notation

$$A : x \longrightarrow x^A. \quad . \quad . \quad . \quad (3.60)$$

If B is another such mapping, the operation AB is defined as the result of first performing A and then B, thus

$$AB : x \longrightarrow (x^A)^B (= x^{AB}), \quad . \quad . \quad (3.61)$$

which lays down the *law of composition* for mappings. In general, $AB \neq BA$.

The identical operation I makes every object correspond to itself, thus

$$I : x \longrightarrow x^I (= x).$$

It plays the part of the *unit element* in the set of all mappings of Γ into itself.

We shall now show that any set of mappings A, B, C, ... *obeys the associative law.* Indeed, by a repeated application of (3.61) we have

$$x^{A(BC)} = (x^A)^{BC} = \left((x^A)^B \right)^C$$

and

$$x^{(AB)C} = (x^{AB})^C = \left((x^A)^B \right)^C,$$

i.e.

$$x^{A(BC)} = x^{(AB)C}$$

for all x, and therefore

$$A(BC) = (AB)C.$$

This result allows us to prove by an indirect argument that certain sets of elements or operations satisfy the group postulates, and in particular the associative law. It is only necessary to show that the elements in question may be regarded as mappings of a suitable aggregate Γ into itself.

Example 1.   If Γ is a finite aggregate of n distinct objects, the set of mappings consists of the $n!$ permutations, which therefore form a group (p. 64).

Example 2.   Let Γ be the aggregate of all points in $[n]$-space.   The linear transformation

$$y_i = a_{i1}x_1 + a_{i2}x_2 + \ldots + a_{in}x_n$$

of non-zero determinant $|a_{ik}|$ may be regarded as a mapping of Γ in which the point x is transformed into y.   The set of all these transformations forms an (infinite) group.

An important (infinite) subgroup consists of all transformations which transform the sphere

$$\Gamma_1 : \; x_1^2 + x_2^2 + \ldots + x_n^2 = 1$$

into itself (*orthogonal transformations*).

Example 3.   The functions

$$z, \quad \frac{1}{1-z}, \quad \frac{z-1}{z}, \quad \frac{1}{z}, \quad 1-z, \quad \frac{z}{z-1}$$

where z is a complex variable, may be regarded as a set of mappings of the complex plane Γ (including the point ∞) into itself (see p. 14).

In all these examples the associative law has thus been indirectly established.

28. Groups related to Geometrical Configurations. Suppose we are given a configuration in three-dimensional space, and let us consider rotations about a fixed point O. The set of all rotations that brings the configuration into coincidence with itself, forms a group.   This group is indicative of the symmetry with which the configuration is endowed.   In the absence of any symmetry the group reduces to the identical transformation.

We shall now discuss in more detail some cases of special interest.

(i) **Dihedral Groups.** Consider a plane lamina having the shape of a regular polygon of n vertices, and suppose that the two sides of the lamina are completely alike. (Figure 2 illustrates the case in which $n = 6$.) There are

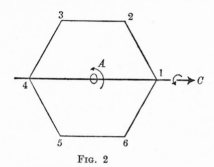

Fig. 2

$2n$ rotations, including the identical operation, which bring the lamina to coincidence with itself. For we may rotate the lamina through one of the angles

$$0, \ \frac{2\pi}{n}, \ 2 \cdot \frac{2\pi}{n}, \ \ldots, \ (n-1)\frac{2\pi}{n}$$

about the line through the centre O and perpendicular to the plane of the lamina. These n operations may be denoted by

$$I, \ A, \ A^2, \ \ldots, \ A^{n-1},$$

where A represents a rotation through $2\pi/n$ and

$$A^n = I. \qquad . \qquad . \qquad . \qquad . \quad (3.62)$$

A further operation consists in reversing the two sides of the lamina. This may be accomplished by a rotation C through π about a line joining the centre to one of the vertices. It must be understood that this line does *not* take part in any rotation but is assumed to retain its orientation in space. To fix the ideas, let us take 01 as the axis of the rotation C. We have

$$C^2 = I, \qquad . \qquad . \qquad . \qquad . \quad (3.63)$$

since C^2 corresponds to a rotation through 2π, i.e. 0, and the $2n$ operations

$$C^\lambda A^\mu \quad (\lambda = 0, 1 \; ; \; \mu = 0, 1, \ldots, n-1) \qquad . \quad (3.64)$$

represent all possible rotations of the lamina into itself ; for they allow any vertex to be brought into the position of any other vertex with or without reversal of the two sides of the lamina.

In order to complete the multiplication table we have to find a relation between A and C. A little geometrical consideration shows that

$$AC = CA^{-1}, \qquad . \qquad . \qquad . \qquad . \quad (3.65)$$

which in virtue of (3.63) is equivalent to

$$(AC)^2 = I. \qquad . \qquad . \qquad . \qquad . \quad (3.66)$$

(The reader is recommended to verify (3.65) by drawing diagrams analogous to those on p. 8.) We remark that the $2n$ elements of the group might equally well have been denoted by

$$A^\mu C^\lambda \quad (\lambda = 0, 1 \; ; \; \mu = 0, 1, \ldots, n-1), \qquad . \quad (3.67)$$

which on account of (3.65) is evidently equivalent to (3.64). Our results may be summarized as follows :

The rotations which transform a regular n-gonal lamina into itself, form a group of order $2n$. *It is called the* **dihedral group** *of order* $2n$, *and its defining relations are*

$$A^n = C^2 = (AC)^2 = I. \qquad . \qquad . \qquad . \quad (3.68)$$

It will be recalled that the dihedral groups of orders 6 and 8 were introduced in (2.58) and (2.61) respectively, subject to the associative law being confirmed. This has now been done for all dihedral groups, since they may be represented as groups of rotations.

The dihedral group of order 6 is isomorphic with P_3 (p. 69).

It is of interest to obtain analytical expressions for the operations of the dihedral group of order $2n$. If x is a variable ranging over the values 1, 2, ..., n, which denote the vertices of the lamina in counter-clockwise order, the operation A is described * by the congruence relation

$$x^A \equiv x + 1 \pmod{n}. \quad . \quad . \quad . \quad (3.69)$$

Again, if $x = 1 + z$, the image of x under the operation C is given by $x^C \equiv 1 - z$. Thus we have

$$x^C \equiv 2 - x \pmod{n}. \quad . \quad . \quad . \quad (3.70)$$

All relations between the generating elements A and C may be derived from (3.69) and (3.70); e.g., we have

$$x^{AC} = (x^A)^C \equiv (x+1)^C \equiv 2 - (x+1) \equiv 1 - x,$$
$$x^{(AC)^2} = 1 - (1 - x) = x,$$

i.e. $(AC)^2 = I,$

as in (3.66).

(ii) **The Tetrahedral Group.** Consider a regular tetrahedron with vertices 1, 2, 3, 4 which is free to rotate about its centre O. There are twelve rotations which transform the tetrahedron into itself. For one of the vertices, say 1, can be brought into the position of any of the four vertices 1, 2, 3, 4, and the solid can then be rotated through one of the angles 0 or $2\pi/3$ or $4\pi/3$ about the line joining this vertex to the centre, whereby the three faces meeting at the vertex are cyclically interchanged. Thus we have 4×3 operations in all.

Each operation of the tetrahedral group permutes the vertices in some way; it is therefore isomorphic with a subgroup of P_4. If one vertex is fixed, the remaining

---

* The notation x^A has, of course, nothing to do with that for a power of x.

three vertices α, β, γ can only be permuted cyclically. Hence the tetrahedral group includes all possible cycles (α, β, γ). We have seen on p. 78 that these cycles generate the group A_4, which is also of order 12. Thus the tetrahedral group contains A_4, but as it is of the same order as A_4, it follows that the *tetrahedral group is isomorphic with the alternating group* A_4.

(iii) **The Octahedral (Hexahedral) Group.** The centres of the faces of a regular octahedron may be regarded as the vertices of a cube (hexahedron), and conversely to every cube we can inscribe an octahedron whose vertices lie at the centres of the faces of the cube. Hence the two solids have the same properties of symmetry, i.e. if one is transformed into itself, so is the other. Thus *the octahedral and hexahedral groups are identical*, though only the first name is in common use. In the present discussion of this group we find it more convenient to consider a cube than an octahedron.

First, we note that the group of the cube consists of twenty-four operations, because each vertex of the cube may be brought into the position of any of the eight vertices, and when this has been done, the solid may be rotated through one of the angles 0 or $2\pi/3$ or $4\pi/3$ about the diameter through this vertex, giving in all 8×3, i.e. 24, rotations, including the identity.

The four diagonals of the cube are permuted amongst themselves when the cube is transformed into itself. If a diagonal is carried over into itself, it either coincides with the axis of rotation, or else the operation interchanges its two end-points ; in this case the axis of rotation is at right-angles to the diagonal and the angle of rotation is π. We infer that no rotation of the cube can transform each of the four diagonals into itself ; for the axis of such a rotation would have to be at right-angles to at least three diagonals, which is obviously impossible. Hence two distinct rotations of the octahedral group correspond to two distinct permutations of the four diagonals. As there exist only twenty-four permutations of four objects, it follows that *the octahedral group is isomorphic with the symmetric group P_4.*

(iv) **The Icosahedral (Dodecahedral) Group.** Turning now to the last two of the regular polyhedra, we observe that the icosahedron and dodecahedron have the same properties of symmetry. For the centres of the twenty faces of an icosahedron may be joined to form a regular dodecahedron, and conversely, the twelve vertices of an icosahedron can be placed at the centres of the faces of a suitable dodecahedron. Thus *the icosahedral and dodecahedral groups are identical*, and either solid may be used to examine the nature of the group elements. We decide to choose the dodecahedron, with which the reader of this series of University Texts is no doubt more familiar, seeing it, as he does, on the cover of each volume that he takes into his hand.

First of all we remark that the dodecahedral group contains sixty distinct operations. For any vertex may be brought into the position of one of the twenty vertices, and after the vertex has reached its final position, the solid may be rotated about the diameter through it. These operations cause cyclic interchanges of the three faces which meet at the extremities of the diameters. The possible angles of rotation are therefore 0, $2\pi/3$, $4\pi/3$, whence it follows that there are 20×3 ($=60$) distinct rotations (including the identity) which bring the dodecahedron into coincidence with itself.

In Euclid's classical construction * a dodecahedron is derived from a cube in such a way that each of the twelve edges of the cube is a diagonal in one of the faces of the dodecahedron. Conversely, if we start with a given diagonal, we can inscribe in the dodecahedron one, and only one, cube which has this diagonal as one of its edges. Since each face has five diagonals, it follows that five cubes can thus be inscribed. Any rotation of the dodecahedron into itself induces a permutation of the five cubes. Bearing

* Elements, Book XIII, Proposition 17.

in mind that the edges of each cube are in (1, 1)-correspondence with the faces of the dodecahedron, the reader will have no difficulty in convincing himself that no rotation of the latter (except the identity) leaves all five cubes in their original position or merely transforms each cube into itself. Hence different rotations give rise to different permutations of the five cubes, i.e. the dodecahedral group is isomorphic with a certain subgroup of order 60 of the symmetric group P_5. As we shall prove in Chapter IV, Corollary 1, p. 123, that the alternating group A_5 is the only subgroup of P_5 of order 60, we can state that the dodecahedron group is isomorphic with A_5.

Examples

(1) Resolve (i) $\begin{pmatrix} 1 & 2 & 3 & 4 & 5 & 6 & 7 & 8 & 9 \\ 4 & 6 & 9 & 7 & 2 & 5 & 8 & 1 & 3 \end{pmatrix}$ and (ii) $\begin{pmatrix} a & b & c & d & e & f \\ c & e & d & f & b & a \end{pmatrix}$ into cycles. Find the orders of the two given permutations.

(2) Express in terms of mutually exclusive cycles

  (i) $(abc \ldots k)(al)$;

  (ii) $(a_1a_2 \ldots a_r xy b_1 b_2 \ldots b_s)(a_r a_{r-1} \ldots a_1 xy c_1 c_2 \ldots c_t)$;

  (iii) $(a_1a_2 \ldots a_r xyz b_1 b_2 \ldots b_s)(a_r a_{r-1} \ldots a_1 xyz c_1 c_2 \ldots c_t)$.

(3) Verify that the permutations (1 2)(3 4) and (1 3)(2 4) commute.

(4) Show that $(ab \ldots lx)(x\alpha\beta \ldots \lambda) = (ab \ldots l\alpha\beta \ldots \lambda x)$, where $a, b, \ldots, l, x, \alpha, \beta, \ldots, \lambda$ are distinct symbols.

(5) Prove that a cycle of degree m is even or odd according as m is odd or even.

(6) Show that a permutation of degree n which is the product of r cycles (including those of order 1) is even or odd according as $n - r$ is even or odd.

(7) Prove that P_n may be generated by the transpositions

$$(1\ 2),\ (2\ 3), \ldots, (n-1, n).$$

(8) Show that P_n may be generated by the cycle $C = (1\ 2 \ldots n)$ and the transposition $T = (12)$.

(9) Prove that every regular permutation can be expressed as the power of a cycle and that, conversely, if $C = (1\ 2 \ldots m)$, then C^s is a regular permutation consisting of d cycles of degree m' where $d = (m, s)$ and $m' = m/d$.

(10) Let G_i $(i = 1, 2, \ldots, g)$ be the elements of an abstract group G and associate with every element R of G the permutation $\bar{R}$ which changes G_i into $R^{-1}G_i$. Prove that (i) the set of all $\bar{R}$ forms a group $\bar{\mathsf{G}}$ which is isomorphic with G, (ii) every permutation of $\bar{\mathsf{G}}$ commutes with every element of G' (of Cayley's Theorem, p. 80), (iii) a permutation that commutes with every permutation of $\bar{\mathsf{G}}$ belongs to G', and vice versa.

(11) Obtain the group which transforms a rectangular lamina into itself.

(12) Prove that when the g permutations of a transitive group of degree n are written as products of mutually exclusive cycles, they contain between them $(n-1)g$ letters.

HINTS and ANSWERS.   1. (i) $(1\ 4\ 7\ 8)(2\ 6\ 5)(3\ 9)$, (ii) $(a\,c\,d\,f)$ $(b\,e)$, orders 12, 4.   2. (i) $(abc \ldots kl)$, (ii) $(a_r y b_1 \ldots b_s x c_1 \ldots c_t)$, (iii) $(a_r y c_1 c_2 \ldots c_t)(x z b_1 b_2 \ldots b_s)$.   8. Consider the permutations $C^{-r} T C^r$ where $r = 0, 1, \ldots, n-1$.   10. (iii) Let $G_i \longrightarrow f(G_i)$ be such a permutation ; if it commutes with every element of G', we must have $f(G_i P) = f(G_i)P$ for every P of G. Put $G_i = I$.   11. The four-group.   12. In the expansion of G relative to G_1 the letter 1 occurs in all permutations which do not belong to G_1, i.e. $g - g/n$ times ; the same is true for the other letters.

CHAPTER IV

INVARIANT SUBGROUPS

29. Classes of Conjugate Elements. In this and the following chapter we shall again be concerned with general properties of abstract groups.

DEFINITION 1. *Two elements* A *and* B *of a group* G *are said to be* **conjugate** *with respect to* G *if there exists an element* T *in* G *such that*

$$T^{-1}AT = B. \qquad . \qquad . \qquad . \qquad (4.1)$$

The element T, which need not be unique, is called the **transforming element.** We note that the relation of conjugacy is (i) *reflexive*, i.e. A is conjugate with itself because $I^{-1}AI = A$, (ii) *symmetrical*, i.e. if A is conjugate with B, then B is conjugate with A because (4.1) implies that $T_1^{-1}BT_1 = A$ where $T_1 = T^{-1}$, (iii) *transitive*, i.e. if A is conjugate with B and B is conjugate with C, then A is conjugate with C because if $T^{-1}AT = B$ and $S^{-1}BS = C$ it follows that $(TS)^{-1}A(TS) = C$.

We have already seen (p. 22) that conjugate elements are of the same order. Conjugate permutations were considered on p. 70.

The complex which consists of all elements conjugate with A (including A itself) is called the **class** of A and will be denoted by (A), thus

$$(A) = A + T_2^{-1}AT_2 + T_3^{-1}AT_3 + \dots.$$

It is of interest to determine the number of distinct elements in (A). This is best done by enquiring what elements of G commute with A : if N_1 and N_2 are two such elements we have

$$AN_1 = N_1A, \quad AN_2 = N_2A,$$

and therefore

$$A(N_1N_2) = (AN_1)N_2 = (N_1A)N_2 = N_1(AN_2) = (N_1N_2)A,$$

i.e. the product N_1N_2 also commutes with A. Thus *the elements of* **G** *which commute with a fixed element* A *form a subgroup* N_A *of order* n_A, *say*; *it is called the* **normalizer** *of* A. For brevity let us put $N = N_A$ and $n = n_A$. Suppose that the expansion of **G** into cosets relative to **N** is

$$G = NT_1 + NT_2 + \ldots + NT_h \quad (T_1 = I), \quad . \quad (4.2)$$

where $h \ (=g/n)$ is the index of the normalizer. A typical element of NT_i may be written NT_i, where N is any element of **N**, i.e. any element which commutes with A. We have

$$(NT_i)^{-1}A(NT_i) = T_i^{-1}(N^{-1}AN)T_i = T_i^{-1}AT_i,$$

irrespective of the element N chosen. Thus all elements which belong to the same coset in (4.2) transform A alike. Conversely, two elements from different cosets transform A differently. For if not, we should have a relation

$$T_i^{-1}AT_i = T_j^{-1}AT_j,$$

whence

$$A(T_iT_j^{-1}) = (T_iT_j^{-1})A,$$

which means that $T_iT_j^{-1}$ commutes with A and therefore belongs to **N**, i.e. by Chapter II, Lemma 2, p. 34, $NT_i = NT_j$. Thus the index of the normalizer of A is equal to the exact number of distinct conjugates of A. We collect these results in the following statement.

THEOREM 1. *Those elements of* **G** *which commute with a given element* A, *form a subgroup* **N** *of order* n (*the normalizer of* A). *If*

$$G = NT_1 + NT_2 + \ldots + NT_h,$$

where g = nh, *then the class* (A) *contains* h *distinct elements which can be written*

$$T_1^{-1}AT_1, T_2^{-1}AT_2, \ldots, T_h^{-1}AT_h. \quad . \quad (4.3)$$

We might paraphrase this important theorem as follows: let A be a fixed element of G and let X run through the g elements of G. Of the g elements $X^{-1}AX$, which are thus formally obtained, only h are distinct, each occurring n times where n is the order and h the index of the normalizer of A $(g = nh)$.

An element A forms a class by itself $(h = 1)$ if, and only if, its normalizer is identical with the whole group $(g = n)$, i.e. A commutes with all elements of G. Such an element is called an **invariant** or **self-conjugate element** of G. In an Abelian group every element is invariant and the concept of classes becomes illusory. In every group, I is an invariant element, i.e.

$$(I) = I,$$

because $X^{-1}IX = I$ for every element X.

The various classes of conjugate elements are *mutually exclusive*; for if (A) and (B) had an element in common, we should have an equation

$$T^{-1}AT = S^{-1}BS,$$

whence $X^{-1}AX = (ST^{-1}X)^{-1}B(ST^{-1}X)$ for every element X of G. Thus every element of (A) would belong to (B), and by a similar argument we could show that (B) was completely contained in (A). Hence two distinct classes have no element in common. Since each element of G belongs to some class, we have a decomposition of the form

$$G = (A_1) + (A_2) + \ldots + (A_k), \qquad \qquad (4.4)$$

where k is the number of distinct classes. On equating the number of elements on both sides of (4.4) we obtain the important relation

$$g = h_1 + h_2 + \ldots + h_k, \qquad \qquad (4.5)$$

where h_i is the number of elements in (A_i). We repeat that

$$h_i \mid g \quad (i = 1, 2, \ldots, k) \qquad \qquad (4.6)$$

and that $h_i = 1$ if, and only if, A_i is self-conjugate.

The following theorem is a simple application of these results.

THEOREM 2.   *If a group is of order* p^m, *where* p *is a prime, the number of its self-conjugate elements is a positive multiple of* p.

Proof.   In (4.5) each term, being a factor of p^m, is either equal to unity or else is of the form $p^\mu (\mu > 0)$. If there are z terms of the former type, the group has z self-conjugate elements. Hence after suitable rearrangement (4.5) becomes

$$p^m = z + p^\mu + p^{\mu'} + \dots \quad (0 < \mu \leqslant \mu' \leqslant \dots).$$

From this equation it is evident that z must be a multiple of p ; and since I is a self-conjugate element and therefore $z \geqslant 1$, it follows that z is in fact a positive multiple of p.

30. Invariant Subgroups.   The concept of normalizer is not confined to single elements. If K is a given complex of G, any complex of the form $X^{-1}KX$ is said to be conjugate with K relative to G. Those elements of G which commute with K, i.e. for which

$$N^{-1}KN = K \quad \text{or} \quad KN = NK,$$

form a group N which is called the **normalizer** of K in G. In analogy to Theorem 1 we have

THEOREM 3.   *The number of distinct complexes conjugate with K is equal to the index of its normalizer.*

A complex which commutes with every element of G ($N = G$) is said to be **invariant** or **self-conjugate** in G. In particular, if the complex is a subgroup we have

DEFINITION 2.   *A subgroup* H *is called an* **invariant** (*or* **normal** *or* **self-conjugate**) **subgroup** *of* G *if it commutes with every element of* G, *i.e. if*

$$HX = XH \quad \text{or} \quad X^{-1}HX = H \quad . \quad . \quad (4.7)$$

for every element X *of* G.

II

It should be noted that (4.7) is a relation between *complexes*, i.e. if H is an element of H, the condition of invariance demands that $X^{-1}HX$ should be some element H' of H, not necessarily H itself.

If A is any subgroup of G whatsoever, the groups (see Chapter II, Theorem 2, p. 33)

$$X^{-1}AX, \quad Y^{-1}AY, \quad Z^{-1}AZ, \ldots$$

are called the **conjugate subgroups** of A. Thus *a subgroup is invariant if, and only if, it coincides with all its conjugate subgroups.* The two improper subgroups I and G are invariant subgroups of G.

In an Abelian group all subgroups are invariant. We shall use the symbolical notation

$$H \lessdot G \quad \text{or} \quad G \gtrdot H$$

to express that H is an invariant subgroup of G.

We should like to emphasize once more that the concept of invariance is a relative one, i.e. if $H \lessdot G$ and $H \subset G_1 \subset G \subset G_0$, it must not be taken for granted that H is an invariant subgroup of G_0; on the other hand, we have of course $H \lessdot G_1$.

If H is an invariant subgroup and

$$X = X_1 + X_2 + \ldots + X_m$$

any complex of G, we have $X_i H = H X_i$, whence on summing over i,

$$XH = HX. \quad \ldots \quad \ldots \quad (4.8)$$

Using (4.7) and the rules (2.36) and (2.41), we obtain the following results:

(i) *if* $H_1 \lessdot G$, $H_2 \lessdot G$, $\ldots$, *then* $H_1 \cap H_2 \cap \ldots \lessdot G$.

(ii) *if* $K_1, K_2, \ldots$ *are invariant complexes, then* $\{K_1, K_2, \ldots\}$ *is an invariant subgroup.*

The invariant subgroups arrived at under (i) and (ii) might well be improper subgroups.

The following simple fact is frequently used:

THEOREM 4. *A subgroup of index* 2 *is always an invariant subgroup.*

Proof. Let H be a subgroup of G of index 2 so that there are only two cosets of G relative to H. Thus if S is any element of G that does not belong to H, neither HS nor SH has an element in common with H. Hence

$$G = H + HS \quad \text{and} \quad G = H + SH.$$

It follows that

$$HS = SH.$$

In addition we have $HH = HH$ for every element H of H (see (2.14), p. 32), and hence also $H(HS) = (HS)H$. Since every element X of G is either of the form H or HS, we infer that $HX = XH$ is universally true, i.e. H is an invariant subgroup.

Example 1. In the dihedral group

$$D_{2n} : A^n = C^2 = (AC)^2 = I,$$

the cyclic group $A = \{A\}$ of order n is an invariant subgroup of index 2.

Example 2. The alternating group A_n is an invariant subgroup of P_n.

If A belongs to an invariant subgroup H, so does every element of the form $X^{-1}AX$, where X is an arbitrary element of G, i.e. each element of the class (A) is contained in H. *Thus an invariant subgroup is composed of complete classes of G*

$$H = (I) + (A) + (B) + \ldots$$

and conversely, if the sum of several such classes satisfies the group postulates, it constitutes an invariant subgroup of G.

Example 3. The twenty-four elements of P_4 are to be arranged according to classes as follows :

$$K_0 = I$$
$$K_1 = (1\ 2) + (1\ 3) + (1\ 4) + (2\ 3) + (2\ 4) + (3\ 4)$$
$$K_2 = (1\ 2\ 3) + (1\ 2\ 4) + (1\ 3\ 2) + (1\ 3\ 4) + (1\ 4\ 2)$$
$$+ (1\ 4\ 3) + (2\ 3\ 4) + (2\ 4\ 3)$$

$K_3 = (1\ \ 2)(3\ \ 4) + (1\ \ 3)(2\ \ 4) + (1\ \ 4)(2\ \ 3)$
$K_4 = (1\ \ 2\ \ 3\ \ 4) + (1\ \ 2\ \ 4\ \ 3) + (1\ \ 3\ \ 2\ \ 4) + (1\ \ 3\ \ 4\ \ 2)$
$$+ (1\ \ 4\ \ 2\ \ 3) + (1\ \ 4\ \ 3\ \ 2).$$

It can be verified that the complex

$$V = K_0 + K_3 = I + (1\ \ 2)(3\ \ 4) + (1\ \ 3)(2\ \ 4) + (1\ \ 4)(2\ \ 3) \quad (4.9)$$

forms a group (see p. 82); this is therefore an invariant subgroup of P_4.

31. The Quotient (Factor) Group. Let H be an invariant subgroup of G and consider the decomposition

$$G = HS_1 + HS_2 + \ldots + HS_n \quad (S_1 = I), \qquad . \quad (4.10)$$

where $g = hn$. Now consider the product $(HS_i)(HS_j)$. Since, by (4.7), $S_iH = HS_i$, we find that

$$(HS_i)(HS_j) = HHS_iS_j = HS_iS_j,$$

using (2.17), p. 33. The last expression is of the form HX and is therefore equal to one of the terms in (4.10), say

$$H(S_iS_j) = HS_k.$$

Thus we have

$$(HS_i)(HS_j) = HS_k. \qquad . \qquad . \qquad (4.11)$$

This result is of fundamental importance as it allows us to regard the n cosets

$$HS_1, HS_2, \ldots, HS_n \quad (S_1 = I) \qquad . \qquad (4.12)$$

as elements of a *group* of order n. Its multiplication table is typified by (4.11); the *unit element* of this group is H because

$$H(HS) = H^2S = HS$$

and

$$(HS)H = HHS = HS$$

by (4.7). Any complex HX is equal to one of the cosets (4.12) even if X is not one of the elements S. Thus the *inverse* of HS may be written in the form HS^{-1}, because

$$(HS)(HS^{-1}) = H^2SS^{-1} = H,$$

and we infer that it, too, belongs to the set (4.12), though it may there have been expressed differently. Finally we remark that the *associative law* is fulfilled, having been generally established for complexes in Chapter II ((2.7), p. 30). The group (4.12) is called the **quotient group** of G *relative to* H or the **factor group** *of* H *in* G and is denoted by G/H. Its order is g/h $(=n)$.

It should be noted that equation (4.11), which leads to the idea of a quotient group, is essentially based on the invariance of H. The term quotient group and the symbol G/H will not be used unless H is an invariant subgroup of G.

Example. In example 3 on p. 101 the cosets of P_4 relative to the invariant subgroup V can be expressed as follows :

$$V_1 = V = I + (1\ 2)(3\ 4) + (1\ 3)(2\ 4) + (1\ 4)(2\ 3),$$
$$V_2 = V(1\ 2\ 3) = (1\ 2\ 3) + (1\ 3\ 4) + (2\ 4\ 3) + (1\ 4\ 2),$$
$$V_3 = V(1\ 3\ 2) = (1\ 3\ 2) + (2\ 3\ 4) + (1\ 2\ 4) + (1\ 4\ 3),$$
$$V_4 = V(1\ 2) = (1\ 2) + (3\ 4) + (1\ 3\ 2\ 4) + (1\ 4\ 2\ 3),$$
$$V_5 = V(1\ 3) = (1\ 3) + (1\ 2\ 3\ 4) + (2\ 4) + (1\ 4\ 3\ 2),$$
$$V_6 = V(1\ 4) = (1\ 4) + (1\ 2\ 4\ 3) + (1\ 3\ 4\ 2) + (2\ 3).$$

The reader may verify that the six cosets V_i $(i = 1, 2, \ldots, 6)$ form a group, namely P_4/V, which is isomorphic with P_3 (see Table 4, p. 15), e.g.,

$$V_2 V_6 = V(1\ 2\ 3)(1\ 4) = V(1\ 2\ 3\ 4) = V(1\ 3) = V_5.$$

32. The Centre. The aggregate of self-conjugate elements of G, including I, forms an *Abelian* group Z, which is called the **centre** of G. For if A and B are self-conjugate elements, we have $X^{-1}AX = A$ and $X^{-1}BX = B$ for every element X of G, and therefore

$$X^{-1}(AB)X = (X^{-1}AX)(X^{-1}BX) = AB,$$

which proves the group property. Also $B^{-1}AB = A$, i.e.

$$AB = BA.$$

Alternatively, *the centre may be defined as the aggregate of those elements of* **G** *which commute with all elements of* **G**. In some groups the centre reduces to the single element I, while the opposite extreme occurs in Abelian groups where $Z = G$. The centre is, so to speak, the Abelian part of a group.

The centre is always an invariant subgroup, because the equation $X^{-1}ZX = Z$ is certainly satisfied, since in fact $X^{-1}ZX = Z$ for each element of Z.

As an application of these ideas we shall prove:

THEOREM 5. *A group of order* p^2, *where* p *is a prime, is always Abelian.*

Proof. By Theorem 2, the order of the centre of a group of order p^2 is either p^2 or p. The former alternative is equivalent to saying that the whole group **G** is identical with **Z** and is therefore Abelian. It remains to investigate whether **Z** can be of order p. The quotient group **G**/**Z** is then of order p^2/p, i.e. p, and hence is a cyclic group. Thus we may write

$$G = Z + ZP + \ldots + ZP^{p-1}.$$

Two typical elements of **G** may be written

$$G_1 = Z_1 P^\lambda, \quad G_2 = Z_2 P^\mu,$$

where Z_1 and Z_2 belong to **Z** and therefore commute with all elements of **G**. Hence

$$G_1 G_2 = Z_1 Z_2 P^{\lambda+\mu} = Z_2 Z_1 P^{\lambda+\mu} = G_2 G_1,$$

i.e. **G** is Abelian, and **Z** is of order p^2 after all.

33. The Commutator Group. Corresponding to any two elements S and T of **G**, we define a **commutator** U by the equation

$$U = S^{-1}T^{-1}ST. \qquad \qquad (4.13)$$

Evidently $U = I$ if, and only if, $ST = TS$. In an Abelian group all commutators are equal to the unit element.

Suppose that on making S and T run independently through the whole group we obtain the commutators

$$U_1, U_2, \ldots, U_m. \qquad . \qquad . \qquad . \quad (4.14)$$

It is possible that the product of two commutators cannot itself be written as a commutator. But in any case *the set of all commutators generates a certain group*

$$U = \{U_1, U_2, \ldots, U_m\},$$

which is called the **commutator group** *of* G. If $U = G$, the group G is called a **perfect group**.

THEOREM 6. *The commutator group is an invariant subgroup, and its quotient group is Abelian; it is contained in every invariant subgroup which has an Abelian quotient group.*

Proof. (i) If X is any element of G and if U is a typical commutator, we have

$$X^{-1}UX = X^{-1}S^{-1}T^{-1}STX = S_1^{-1}T_1^{-1}S_1T_1,$$

where $S_1 = X^{-1}SX$ and $T_1 = X^{-1}TX$. Hence $X^{-1}UX$ is also a commutator, i.e.

$$X^{-1}UX = U,$$

which proves that U is an invariant subgroup of G.

(ii) The elements of G/U are the complexes UX; the commutator of two such complexes can be written

$$(UX^{-1})(UY^{-1})(UX)(UY) = UX^{-1}Y^{-1}XY, \quad . \quad (4.15)$$

in virtue of the multiplication table for the quotient group. Now $X^{-1}Y^{-1}XY$ is itself an element of U and may therefore be absorbed by the factor U on the right-hand side of (4.15). Hence in G/U every commutator is equal to U, which is the unit element of that group, i.e. G/U is Abelian.

(iii) If R is any invariant subgroup of G whose quotient group is Abelian, then by the preceding argument

$$RX^{-1}Y^{-1}XY = R,$$

i.e. R contains $X^{-1}Y^{-1}XY$, and hence all products of such elements, thus $R \supset U$.

We conclude this section by proving the following result.

THEOREM 7. *If* A *and* B *are two invariant subgroups which have only the unit element in common, then every element of* A *commutes with every element of* B.

Proof. Consider the commutator

$$U = A^{-1}B^{-1}AB = (A^{-1}B^{-1}A)B = A^{-1}(B^{-1}AB),$$

where A and B are typical elements of A and B.

Since A and B are invariant, $A^{-1}B^{-1}A$ is an element of B and $B^{-1}AB$ is an element of A. Thus it appears that U is an element both of A and of B. By hypothesis it must then be equal to I, i.e. A and B commute.

34. Homomorphisms and Isomorphisms.* The idea of isomorphism has already been introduced on p. 19. If G and G′ are *isomorphic* groups, we shall write

$$G \sim G'.$$

The mapping of G onto G′ can be uniquely reversed, i.e. no two elements have the same image. But the typical feature of the mapping is the *conservation of structure*, which is most concisely expressed by

$$(AB)' = A'B' \quad . \quad \quad . \quad \quad . \quad (4.16)$$

(see p. 19). Any mapping $G \longrightarrow G'$ which satisfies condition (4.16) is called a **homomorphic** mapping (or a **homomorphism**) of G onto G′. This includes cases in which two different elements of G may have the same image in G′. Thus in a homomorphism structure is retained but individuality may be destroyed.

To mention a trivial case, we can map any group G onto the group whose only element is the number 1 ; in fact, if $A \longrightarrow 1$, $B \longrightarrow 1$, $C \longrightarrow 1$, ... a relation of the form $AB = C$

---

* In this section the groups may be finite or infinite.

is carried over into $1 \times 1 = 1$, which is evidently true. A rather less obvious example is furnished by the alternating character (Chapter III, Theorem 4, p. 74) of a group of permutations, or by the homomorphic correspondence between a square matrix and its determinant in a group of matrices, where the multiplication theorem of determinants, namely

$$| AB | = | A | \ | B |,$$

is the realization of (4.16).

We shall now prove that if H is an invariant subgroup of G, then G can be homomorphically mapped on to G/H. In fact, if we construct the mapping

$$X \longrightarrow HX, \quad . \qquad . \qquad . \qquad (4.17)$$

where X is a typical element of G, we see that corresponding to a relation $XY = Z$ we have

$$(HX)(HY) = H^2XY = HXY = HZ, . \qquad . \quad (4.18)$$

which shows that condition (4.16) is fulfilled. It should be observed that, in accordance with our definition (4.17), all elements of G which belong to the same coset relative to H have the same image ; for two such elements are of the form H_1X and H_2X respectively, where H_1 and H_2 are any elements of H. Hence by (4.17)

$$H_1X \longrightarrow HH_1X = HX$$
$$H_2X \longrightarrow HH_2X = HX.$$

It is an interesting fact that, in a sense, all homomorphisms are equivalent to those which are generated by suitable invariant subgroups as in (4.17). Suppose we are given a homomorphic mapping $G \longrightarrow G'$ which is typified by

$$X \longrightarrow X'. \quad . \qquad . \qquad . \qquad (4.19)$$

It is clear that the image of the unit element I of G is the unit element I' of G' ; for since $I^2 = I$, the image of I must satisfy the equation $(X')^2 = X'$, which has no solution apart from I'. Again, since $XX^{-1} = I$ is carried over into $X'(X^{-1})' = I'$, we infer that $(X^{-1})' = (X')^{-1}$, i.e.

$$X^{-1} \longrightarrow (X')^{-1}. \qquad . \qquad . \qquad . \quad (4.20)$$

If the homomorphism (4.19) is not an isomorphism, I' is the image of several elements of G. *Let*

$$E = I + E_i + E_j + \ldots \qquad . \qquad . \qquad . \quad (4.21)$$

be the complex of all elements of G *which are mapped on* I'. *We shall show that* E *is an invariant subgroup of* G. For if E_i and E_j are any two elements of E, we have $E_i \longrightarrow I'$ and $E_j \longrightarrow I'$, whence by (4.16) $E_iE_j \longrightarrow I'I' = I'$, which shows that the complex (4.21) is a subgroup. Next, if E is a typical element of E and X any element of G whatsoever, we find, with the aid of (4.20), that

$$X^{-1}EX \longrightarrow (X')^{-1}I'X' = I'.$$

Hence all elements of the form $X^{-1}EX$ belong to E, i.e. E is an invariant subgroup.

Finally, we shall prove that G/E is isomorphic with G'. Consider the mapping

$$EX \longrightarrow X' \qquad . \qquad . \qquad . \qquad . \quad (4.22)$$

between these groups, where X' is the image of X in accordance with the mapping (4.19) of G onto G'. We have already seen that (4.22) leaves all structural relations unaltered. For on putting $H = E$ in (4.18), we have $(EX)(EY) = E(XY)$, which may be interpreted as $X'Y' = (XY)'$. Moreover, distinct elements of G/E have distinct images in G'; indeed, if we had $EX \longrightarrow X'$ and $EY \longrightarrow X'$, our construction of (4.22) would imply that $X \longrightarrow X'$ and $Y \longrightarrow X'$ in the mapping (4.19), whence $XY^{-1} \longrightarrow X'X'^{-1} = I'$; i.e. XY^{-1} would belong to E, and consequently $EX = EY$. Thus the groups G/E and G' are isomorphic.

The group E defined in (4.21) is called the **kernel** of the homomorphism (4.19). We may summarize these results as follows:

THEOREM 8. *If H is an invariant subgroup of G, then G can be homomorphically mapped onto G/H. In any homomorphism G $\longrightarrow$ G', those elements of G which are mapped on the unit element of G' form an invariant subgroup E of G such that G/E is isomorphic with G'.*

The mapping (4.17) is often called a **natural homomorphism**.

35. Automorphisms.* An interesting type of isomorphism occurs when the group of images coincides with the given group G.

DEFINITION 3. *A (1, 1)-mapping Φ of a group G onto itself which associates with every element A of G a unique image A$_\phi$ in G,*

$$\Phi : A \longrightarrow A_\phi$$

is called an **automorphism** *if*

$$(AB)_\phi = A_\phi B_\phi.$$

It follows from the general results of Chapter III, § 27, that the set of automorphisms forms a group.

There are two types of automorphism : if X is a fixed element of G, the mapping

$$\Xi : A \longrightarrow X^{-1}AX\,(=A_\xi),$$

which evidently satisfies the above condition, is called an **inner** automorphism.   In the case of an Abelian group all inner automorphisms reduce to the identical mapping $(A_\xi = A)$.   An automorphism which is not equivalent to the transformation by a single element is said to be an **outer** automorphism.

E.g., in the four-group $A^2 = B^2 = I$, $AB = BA$, the mapping $I \longrightarrow I$, $A \longrightarrow B$, $B \longrightarrow A$, $AB \longrightarrow BA\,(=AB)$ is an outer automorphism.

Again, in a cyclic group $\{A\}$ of order m the correspondence $A \longrightarrow A^k$

* See footnote on p. 106.

constitutes an outer automorphism provided that k is prime to m.

36. The Isomorphism Theorems. * In this section H is a fixed invariant subgroup of G, and we consider the natural homomorphism

$$X \rightarrow (HX) \qquad . \qquad . \qquad . \qquad (4.23)$$

of G on to the quotient group $G' = G/H$. For the time being we shall use the bracket notation (HX) for a single element of the quotient group G' to distinguish it from the complex

$$HX = H_i X + H_j X + \dots.$$

which stands for a collection of elements of G.

Let

$$A = I + A + B + \dots$$

be a subgroup of G. The images of the elements of A form a complex

$$A' = (H) + (HA) + (HB) + \dots \qquad . \qquad . \qquad (4.24)$$

of G', which is in fact a subgroup of G' because

$$(HA)(HB) = (HAB), \qquad . \qquad . \qquad (4.25)$$

and $AB \subset A$.

Now it follows from the remarks on p. 107 that the elements of G whose images belong to A' make up the complex

$$HA = H + HA + HB + \dots \qquad . \qquad . \qquad (4.26)$$

Since H is invariant, we have

$$HA = AH$$

and, by the Product Theorem (p. 56), HA is a subgroup of G. Evidently, HA contains H as an invariant subgroup and its decomposition into cosets relative to H is exhibited by (4.26). Thus we have

$$HA/H = (H) + (HA) + (HB) + \dots = A'. \qquad . \qquad (4.27)$$

It is clear that (4.23) expresses a homomorphic mapping

$$A \rightarrow (HA)$$

* See footnote on p. 106.

of A on to A'. The kernel of this homomorphism consists of those elements E of A for which

$$(HE) = (H).$$

This happens if, and only if, $E \subset H$, and the kernel is therefore

$$D = H \cap A$$

Applying Theorem 8, we learn that D is an invariant subgroup of A—a fact which can easily be verified directly—and that the groups A/D and A' are isomorphic. Thus we have proved

THEOREM 9 (**First Isomorphism Theorem**). *If $H \lessgtr G$ and if A is any subgroup of G, then $H \cap A$ is an invariant subgroup of A and*

$$A/(H \cap A) \sim HA/H.$$

Next, let A be a subgroup between H and G, i.e.

$$H \subset A \subset G.$$

Since H is invariant in G, it is automatically invariant in A, and if

$$A = H + HA + HB + \ldots$$

is the decomposition of A relative to H, then

$$A/H = (H) + (HA) + (HB) + \ldots .$$

Hence A/H is a subgroup of G'. Conversely, let

$$A' = (H) + (HA) + (HB) + \ldots$$

be a subgroup of G/H, whose multiplication table is typified by

$$(HA)(HB) = (HC). \qquad . \qquad . \qquad . \quad (4.28)$$

If this equation is interpreted as a relation between elements of G, it becomes

$$HAHB = HC. \qquad . \qquad . \qquad . \quad (4.29)$$

Now the complex

$$A = H + HA + HB + \ldots$$

is a subgroup of G. For two typical elements of A may be denoted by H_1A and H_2B and by (4.29) we have

$$H_1A \; H_2B = H_3C,$$

which proves that A is a group. Evidently H is an invariant subgroup of A and we have

$$A' = A/H.$$

Summarizing these results, we have

THEOREM 10. *Let $H \lessdot G$ and let A be a subgroup of G such that $H \subset A \subset G$. Then A/H is a subgroup of G/H. Conversely, every subgroup of G/H is of the form A/H, where A is a suitable group between H and G.*

We shall now investigate the case in which A contains H and is an invariant subgroup of G.

THEOREM 11 (**Second Isomorphism Theorem**). *If $H \lessdot G$ and $H \lessdot A \lessdot G$, then* (i) $A/H \lessdot G/H$ *and* (ii) $\dfrac{G/H}{A/H} \sim G/A$. *Conversely, every invariant subgroup of G/H is of the form A/H, where*

$$H \lessdot A \lessdot G.$$

Proof. The correspondence

$$(HX) \rightarrow (AX) \qquad . \qquad . \qquad . \quad (4.30)$$

associates a definite element of G/A with every element of G/H. For if $HX = HX_1$, then $XX_1^{-1} \subset H$, and hence $XX_1^{-1} \subset A$ whence $AX = AX_1$. Moreover, (4.30) is a homomorphic mapping because

$$(HX)(HY) = (HXY) \rightarrow (AXY) = (AX)(AY).$$

The kernel consists of all those elements of G/H which are mapped on the unit element of G/A, i.e. on A. If (HX) belongs to the kernel we must have $AX = A$. This happens if, and only if, X is an element of A, say $X = A$. Hence the kernel consists of the complexes (HA) and is therefore identical with the group A/H. By Theorem 8 this group is an invariant subgroup of G/H, i.e.

$$A/H \lessdot G/H,$$

and we have the isomorphism

$$\frac{G/H}{A/H} \sim G/A.$$

Conversely, suppose that

$$A' = (H) + (HA) + (HB) + \dots$$

is an invariant subgroup of G/H, so that if X is an arbitrary element of G,

$$(HX)(HA)(HX^{-1}) = (HA_1), \qquad . \quad . \ (4.31)$$

where A_1 is a suitable element of A. The argument leading to Theorem 9 shows that the complex

$$A = H + HA + HB + \dots$$

is a subgroup of G and it remains to prove that it is in fact an invariant subgroup of G. We may interpret (4.31) as a relation between elements of G, i.e. we omit the brackets, and then select the unit element of H in the first and third factor on the left-hand side of (4.31). Thus we get

$$X(HA)X^{-1} \subset HA_1,$$

and similarly

$$X(HB)X^{-1} \subset HB_1. \dots$$

It follows that

$$XAX^{-1} \subset H + HA_1 + HB_1 + \dots \subset A.$$

Similarly, on replacing X by X^{-1} we infer that $XAX^{-1} \subset A$, i.e. $A \subset X^{-1}AX$, and hence $A = X^{-1}AX$. Thus A is an invariant subgroup, which proves the theorem.

37. The Jordan-Hölder Composition Theorem. It is common practice in mathematics to study complex entities by resolving them into simpler components which in some sense are themselves irreducible. Thus integers are decomposed into primes, polynomials are split up into irreducible factors relative to a given field, and so on. But such a resolution is not of great value unless it possesses the property of *uniqueness* in a well-defined manner.

There are several methods of reducing groups. However, we must confine ourselves to one particular line of approach which is due to C. Jordan and was subsequently elaborated by O. Hölder.

DEFINITION 4. *A group which possesses no proper invariant subgroup is called a* **simple** *group*.

The (cyclic) groups of prime order afford trivial instances of simple groups, as they have no proper subgroups at all (Corollary 2, p. 38). Simple groups of composite order are rather rare and command special interest (see Theorem 13, p. 120).

DEFINITION 5. *An invariant subgroup A is called a* **maximum invariant subgroup** *of G if there exists no invariant subgroup H other than G or A such that*

$$G \succ H \succ A. \qquad . \qquad . \qquad . \qquad (4.32)$$

By Theorem 10, (4.32) is equivalent to the statement that G/A has a proper invariant subgroup H/A. Hence we have the following result.

CRITERION. *The subgroup A is a maximum invariant subgroup of G if, and only if, G/A is a simple group.*

A group may well possess several maximum invariant subgroups differing both in structure and order.

If G/A is of prime order, then A is a maximum invariant subgroup.

If G is *not* a simple group, it has a proper invariant subgroup and therefore also a maximum invariant subgroup A, say. Thus

$$G \succ A \succ I. \qquad . \qquad . \qquad . \qquad (4.33)$$

It may happen that A is a simple group; if not, we have

$$A \succ A_1,$$

where A_1 is a maximum invariant subgroup of A. Continuing in this way, we arrive at the result that *every group G possesses a* **composition series**, *i.e. a series of subgroups*

$$G \succ A \succ A_1 \succ \ldots \succ A_{r-1} \succ A_r \succ I, \quad . \quad . \quad (4.34)$$

where

$$G/A, \quad A/A_1, \ldots, A_{r-1}/A_r, \quad A_r \quad . \quad . \quad (4.35)$$

are simple groups, which we shall call **composition-quotient-groups**. It should be clearly understood that while A_i is a (maximum) invariant subgroup of A_{i-1}, it need not be invariant with respect to $G, A, A_1, A_2, \ldots, A_{i-2}$.

If the orders of the groups (4.34) are

$$g, a, a_1, \ldots, a_{r-1}, a_r, \quad . \quad . \quad . \quad (4.36)$$

the orders of the quotient groups are

$$g/a, a/a_1, \ldots, a_{r-1}/a_r, a_r . \quad . \quad . \quad (4.37)$$

respectively. These integers are known as the **composition indices**. Notice that their product is equal to g.

The following fundamental theorem deals with the uniqueness property of composition series referred to at the beginning of this section.

THEOREM 12 (Jordan-Hölder). *In any two composition series for a group G the composition-quotient-groups are, apart from their sequence, isomorphic in pairs.*

Let us consider in more detail what this theorem implies : suppose that

$$G \succ A \succ A_1 \succ \ldots \succ A_r \succ I . \quad . \quad . \quad (I)$$

and

$$G \succ B \succ B_1 \succ \ldots \succ B_s \succ I . \quad . \quad . \quad (II)$$

are two composition series for G. It is then asserted that when suitably arranged the quotient groups

$$G/A, A/A_1, \ldots, A_{r-1}/A_r, A_r \quad . \quad . \quad (III)$$

and

$$G/B, B/B_1, \ldots, B_{s-1}/B_s, B_s \quad . \quad . \quad (IV)$$

I

are isomorphic in pairs. In particular, it would follow that $r = s$, and that the composition indices

$$g/a, \ a/a_1, \ \ldots, \ a_{r-1}/a_r, \ a_r$$

are, possibly after rearrangement, identical with

$$g/b, \ b/b_1, \ \ldots, \ b_{s-1}/b_s, \ b_s.$$

It was this last fact which was discovered by Jordan, while Hölder later observed that the quotient groups were not only of the same order but actually isomorphic.

Proof. Since the only group of order 2, namely the cyclic group C_2, is simple and possesses the *unique* composition series $C_2 \succ I$, we have a basis for induction, and we shall henceforth assume that the theorem has already been proved for groups of order less than g.

If G is simple, the only possible composition series is $G \succ I$, and the theorem is certainly true. If G is not simple, we have to distinguish two cases with regard to (I) and (II):

(i) $A = B$. In this case the series (III) and (IV) become

$$G/A, \ \big| \ A/A_1, \ \ldots, \ A_{r-1}/A_r, \ A_r \qquad . \qquad . \qquad \text{(V)}$$

and

$$G/A, \ \big| \ A/B_1, \ \ldots, \ B_{s-1}/B_s, \ B_s \qquad . \qquad . \qquad \text{(VI)}$$

respectively. Since we assume that the theorem holds for A, the quotient groups on the right of the vertical line are isomorphic in pairs as they represent composition series for A. In particular we have $r = s$, and since the leading terms of the two series are not only isomorphic, but actually identical, we conclude that the complete series are equivalent in the sense of the theorem.

(ii) $A \neq B$. We have seen (p. 111) that

$$C = AB$$

is an invariant subgroup of G which in turn contains A as an invariant subgroup, thus

$$G \succ C \succ A.$$

But since A is a maximum invariant subgroup of G, we must have either $C = A$ or $C = G$. The former alternative must be rejected because B and consequently AB differs from A. Hence we conclude that

$$G = C = AB.$$

Putting $D = A \cap B$ as in Theorem 9, we have

$$G/A \sim B/D \quad \text{and} \quad G/B \sim A/D. \qquad . \qquad (4.38)$$

Since by the Criterion on p. 114 G/A and G/B are simple groups, so are B/D and A/D, i.e. D *is a maximum invariant subgroup both of B and of A*. Let

$$D \succ D_1 \succ \ldots \succ D_t \succ I$$

be any composition series for D whatsoever and consider the following composition series for G :

$$G \succ A \succ D \succ D_1 \succ \ldots \succ D_t \succ I \qquad . \qquad \text{(VII)}$$

and

$$G \succ B \succ D \succ D_1 \succ \ldots \succ D_t \succ I \qquad . \qquad \text{(VIII)}$$

having the quotient groups

$$G/A, \, A/D \mid , \, D/D_1, \ldots, D_t$$

and

$$G/B, \, B/D \mid , \, D/D_1, \ldots, D_t$$

respectively. The groups on the right of the division line are identical in the two series, while those on the left are isomorphic when arranged crosswise in pairs, as stated in (4.38). Let us write

$$\text{(VII)} \sim \text{(VIII)} \qquad . \qquad . \qquad . \qquad (4.39)$$

to express that these two series have the property demanded by the theorem. Since they have the first two terms in common with (I) and (II) respectively, we may appeal to the hypothesis of induction and state that

$$\text{(I)} \sim \text{(VII)} \quad \text{and} \quad \text{(II)} \sim \text{(VIII)}.$$

Combining these results with (4.39), we deduce that $\text{(I)} \sim \text{(II)}$. This completes the proof of the Jordan-Hölder theorem.

Example 1. *The alternating group A_n is a maximum invariant subgroup of P_n.* We have already seen (p. 101) that $P_n \succ A_n$. Since P_n/A_n is of order 2, it follows from the Criterion on p. 114 that A_n is a maximum invariant subgroup of P_n. Let us find a composition series in the cases where n is equal to 3 or 4.

(i) $n = 3$. A composition series for P_3 can evidently be written

$$P_3 \succ A_3 \succ I, \quad . \quad . \quad . \quad . \quad (4.40)$$

the composition-quotient-groups being the simple groups

$$P_3/A_3, \ A_3 \quad . \quad . \quad . \quad . \quad (4.41)$$

of prime orders (composition indices)

$$2, 3 \ . \quad . \quad . \quad . \quad . \quad (4.42)$$

respectively.

(ii) $n = 4$. The group

$$V : I, \ (1\ 2)(3\ 4), \ (1\ 3)(2\ 4), \ (1\ 4)(2\ 3) \quad . \quad (4.43)$$

is an invariant subgroup of P_4 (example on p. 102). As it consists of even permutations, it is an invariant subgroup of A_4. Again, every element of V, other than I, generates a subgroup of V which is of index 2, and is therefore invariant with respect to V. Hence

$$P_4 \succ A_4 \succ V \succ \{(1\ 2)(3\ 4)\} \succ I \quad . \quad . \quad (4.44)$$

is a composition series for P_4 with composition indices

$$2, 3, 2, 2. \quad . \quad . \quad . \quad . \quad (4.45)$$

Example 2. The cyclic group C_6 which is generated by an element A, where $A^6 = I$, possesses a composition series of the form

$$C_6 \succ \{A^2\} \succ I. \ . \quad . \quad . \quad . \quad (4.46)$$

The middle term is a cyclic group of order 3, and the quotient groups of (4.46) are cyclic groups of orders 2 and 3 respectively.

We observe that the quotient groups of (4.40) and (4.46) are isomorphic. Thus we learn that a knowledge of the composition-quotient-groups does not suffice for a reconstruction of the whole group.

DEFINITION 6. *A group G is said to be* **soluble** *if all its composition indices are prime.*

E.g., we see from (4.42) and (4.45) that the groups P_3 and P_4 are soluble.

The decision regarding solubility is often facilitated by the following criterion.

CRITERION. *A group G is soluble if it contains an invariant subgroup H such that H and G/H are soluble.*

Proof. If these conditions are fulfilled we have

$$H \succ H_1 \succ \ldots \succ H_r \succ I \quad . \quad . \quad (4.47)$$

and

$$G/H \succ G_1/H \succ \ldots \succ G_s/H \succ H, \quad . \quad (4.48)$$

where all composition indices in (4.47) and (4.48) are prime. (It should be remembered that any subgroup of G/H can be written in the form A/H and that its unit element is H.) Since by Theorem 11

$$\frac{G_{i-1}/H}{G_i/H} \sim G_{i-1}/G_i \quad (G_0 = G),$$

we infer that

$$G \succ G_1 \succ \ldots \succ G_s \succ H \succ H_1 \succ \ldots \succ H_r \succ I$$

is a composition series for G in which all indices are prime. Hence G is soluble.

38. Galois' Theorem on the Alternating Group. We shall prove in this section that, when $n > 4$, the alternating group A_n contains no proper invariant subgroup. This is equivalent to saying that any invariant subgroup of A_n which does not merely consist of the unit element is equal to A_n. We begin by proving the following lemma.

LEMMA 1. *If an invariant subgroup H of A_n ($n \geqslant 3$) contains one cycle of degree 3, then $H = A_n$.*

Proof. There is no loss of generality in denoting the cycle in question by (1 2 3). When $n = 3$, the alternating group is generated by (1 2 3), and we have nothing further to prove.

Suppose now that $n > 3$. Since H is an invariant subgroup of A_n it contains every permutation of the form

$$S^{-1}(1\ 2\ 3)S,$$

where S is any *even* permutation whatsoever. In particular, if

$$S = (3\ 2\ k),$$

where k is an integer greater than 3, we find that H contains the permutation

$$(3\ 2\ k)^{-1}(1\ 2\ 3)(3\ 2\ k) = (1\ k\ 2)$$

and consequently also its square, namely

$$(1\ 2\ k),\quad (k = 3, 4, \ldots).$$

By Chapter III, Theorem 9 (p. 78), these special cycles generate the alternating group, i.e. $H = A_n$.

We are now in a position to establish the celebrated result referred to in the heading of this section.

THEOREM 13. *When* $n > 4$, A_n *is a simple group.*

Proof. Suppose that H is an invariant subgroup of A_n.

(i) Let H include an element of the form

$$H = ABC\ldots,\qquad \text{.}\qquad \text{.}\qquad \text{.}\qquad \text{(4.49)}$$

where A, B, C, ... are mutually exclusive cycles and

$$A = (a_1 a_2 a_3 a_4 \ldots a_m)\quad \text{and}\quad m > 3.$$

The permutation

$$S = (a_1 a_2 a_3)$$

commutes with all cycles of (4.49) except the first. Since S is even, H also contains the permutations

$$H_1 = S^{-1}HS = (S^{-1}AS)BC\ldots$$

and

$$H_1 H^{-1} = (S^{-1}AS)A^{-1}$$
$$= (a_2 a_3 a_1 a_4 \ldots a_m)(a_m a_{m-1} \ldots a_4 a_3 a_2 a_1)$$
$$= (a_1 a_3 a_m)(a_2)(a_4) \ldots (a_{m-1}) = (a_1 a_3 a_m)$$

(see (3.19), p. 71). Hence we infer from the Lemma that $H = A_n$. From now on we can confine ourselves to cases in which the permutations of H are products of cycles of degrees 2 or 3 only.

(ii) Let H be a permutation of H involving at least two cycles of degree 3. There is no loss of generality in writing

$$H = (1\ 2\ 3)(4\ 5\ 6)P,$$

where P does not depend on the first six numbers. Choosing

$$S = (2\ 3\ 4)$$

as a transforming element and noting that $S^{-1}PS = P$, we deduce that H must also contain the permutations

$$H_1 = S^{-1}HS = (1\ 3\ 4)(2\ 5\ 6)P$$

and

$$H_1 H^{-1} = (1\ 3\ 4)(2\ 5\ 6)(3\ 2\ 1)(6\ 5\ 4) = (1\ 2\ 4\ 3\ 6),$$

contradicting our assumption that no cycles of degree greater than 3 should occur.

(iii) Next consider the case in which H involves only one cycle of degree 3, say

$$H = (1\ 2\ 3)P,$$

where P is a product of mutually exclusive cycles of degree 2 so that $P^2 = I$. We conclude that H contains the permutation

$$H^2 = (1\ 2\ 3)^2 P^2 = (1\ 3\ 2)$$

and therefore, according to the Lemma, coincides with A_n.

(iv) There remains the possibility that H involves no cycles of degree 3, but is a product of transpositions. Such a case does actually occur when $n = 4$ and leads to the four-group V which we discussed on p. 118. On the other hand, when $n > 4$, we can argue as follows : suppose that

$$H = (1\ \ 2)(3\ \ 4)P$$

is an element of H, where P is independent of the numbers 1, 2, 3, 4. If we let

$$S = (2\ \ 3\ \ 4)$$

be a transforming element, we find that H contains the permutations

$$H_1 = S^{-1}HS = (1\ \ 3)(4\ \ 2)P$$

and

$$H_2 = H_1H^{-1} = (1\ \ 3)(4\ \ 2)(1\ \ 2)(3\ \ 4) = (1\ \ 4)(2\ \ 3).$$

Again, on taking

$$T = (1\ \ 4\ \ 5)$$

we conclude that the permutations

$$H_3 = T^{-1}H_2T = (4\ \ 5)(2\ \ 3)$$

and

$$H_3H_2^{-1} = (4\ \ 5)(2\ \ 3)(1\ \ 4)(2\ \ 3) = (4\ \ 5)(1\ \ 4) = (1\ \ 4\ \ 5)$$

also belong to H. Thus it appears that H contains a cycle of degree 3, whence it follows that $H = A_n$. This completes the proof of the theorem.

COROLLARY 1. A_n *is the only subgroup of order* $\frac{1}{2}n!$ *contained in* P_n *when* $n > 4.$*

Proof. Any subgroup H of that order is necessarily an invariant subgroup of P_n (Theorem 4, p. 101). Hence the intersection $D = A_n \cap H$ is an invariant subgroup of A_n. It follows from the above theorem that either $D = I$ or $D = A_n$. As $n > 4$, H contains more than one even permutation and hence has more than one element in common with A_n (Theorem 8, p. 77). Thus $A_n = A_n \cap H$, whence $A_n \subset H$.

* The result is also true when $n \leqslant 4$ (see ex. 7).

But, as both groups are of the same order, we have in fact $A_n = H$.

COROLLARY 2. P_n *is not soluble when* $n > 4$.   For since A_n is simple when $n > 4$,

$$P_n \succ A_n \succ I$$

is a composition series for P_n.   Its composition indices are

$$2, \tfrac{1}{2}n!,$$

the second of which is certainly not prime when $n > 4$.

The concept of soluble groups admits of a very remarkable application in the theory of *algebraical equations*, where it is proved that the general equation of the nth degree can be solved in terms of *radicals* if, and only if, the group P_n is soluble.   We have learned that this condition is fulfilled only when $n = 1, 2, 3, 4$, which explains why there are algebraical " formulae " for solving equations whose degree does not exceed 4.   On the other hand, we are led to the conclusion that no such formulae can possibly exist for the quintic or equations of still higher degree.

Examples

(1) By using Theorem 1 (p. 97) or otherwise, prove that the only permutations of P_n which commute with a given cycle of degree n are the powers of that cycle.

(2) Show that when $n\ (> 2)$ is odd the cycles on n letters form two classes of conjugate elements relative to A_n, each containing $\tfrac{1}{2}(n - 1)!$ members, and that when n is even the cycles on $(n - 1)$ letters are divided into two classes in A_n of $\tfrac{1}{2}n(n - 2)!$ elements each.

(3) Two classes (A) and (A^{-1}), which are generated by inverse elements, are called *inverse* classes.   Prove that (i) inverse classes contain the same number of elements and (ii) a group of even order includes at least one class, other than that consisting of the unit element, which is identical with its inverse class.

(4) Resolve A_4 into classes of conjugate elements.

(5) Show that if $G = G_1 + G_2 + \ldots + G_g$, the group $\{G_1{}^r,$

$G_2{}^r, \ldots, G_g{}^r\}$ is a (proper or improper) invariant subgroup of G.

(6) Let H be an invariant subgroup of index n in G. If R is an element of G such that R^t is the least positive power of R to lie in H, prove that t is a factor both of n and of the order of R.

(7) Prove that A_n is the only subgroup of P_n of index 2, when $n = 2, 3, 4$.

(8) If the commutator C of A and B commutes with both A and B, prove that $(AB)^e = B^e A^e C^{\frac{1}{2}e(e+1)}$.

(9) If each element of a group commutes with every conjugate, show that the commutator of any two elements commutes with both, and prove that the elements whose orders divide a given odd number e, form an invariant subgroup.

(10) Prove that A_4 possesses no subgroup of order 6.

(11) Prove that the commutator group of P_n is A_n.

(12) Find the centre of the quaternion group (Table 12, p. 55), and construct the quotient group relative to the centre. Also obtain a composition series for the quaternion group.

(13) Do the same for the dihedral group of order 8 (Table 11, p. 55).

(14) A group G is defined by $A^4 = B^3 = (AB)^2 = I$. Prove that $N = I + A^2 + B^2 A^2 B + B A^2 B^2$ is an invariant subgroup.

Show that the correspondence

$$A \rightarrow (1234), \quad B \rightarrow (132)$$

maps G homomorphically into P_4.

(15) Continuing the preceding example prove that G/N consists of the six elements

$$N, \quad AN, \quad BN, \quad ABN, \quad BABN, \quad ABAN,$$

and deduce that G and P_4 are in fact isomorphic.

(16) The normalizer of an invariant subgroup is an invariant subgroup.

HINTS and ANSWERS. 2. The normalizers in A_n of such cycles are of orders n and $n-1$ respectively. 4. I, $(1\ 2\ 3) + (1\ 4\ 2) + (1\ 3\ 4) + (2\ 4\ 3)$, $(1\ 3\ 2) + (1\ 2\ 4) + (1\ 4\ 3) + (2\ 3\ 4)$, $(1\ 2)(3\ 4) + (1\ 3)(2\ 4) + (1\ 4)(2\ 3)$. 7. Such a subgroup is invariant and hence consists of complete classes of conjugate elements including the class $K_0 = (I)$. By counting the number of elements in each class of P_n ($n = 1, 2, 3, 4$) it is found that the subgroup must be A_n. (Use the list of classes on pp. 101-

102.)   10. Such a subgroup would have to be invariant, which is incompatible with the result of Example 4.   11. Consider the commutator of $(1\ 2)$ and $(2k)$ and use Theorem 9, p. 78. 12. $I + A^2$; isomorphic with V; G, $\{A^2\}$, I.   13. The same. 15. Since $A^2 \subset N$ and $B^2 = ABA$, the elements of G/N can be brought into the form $A^\alpha B^\beta A^\gamma B^\delta \ldots N$, where α, β, γ, $\delta, \ldots$ are 0 or 1.   The result then follows because $(AB)^2 = I$.

CHAPTER V

SYLOW GROUPS AND PRIME POWER GROUPS

39. A Lemma on Abelian Groups. If G is a group of order g, the order of any subgroup of G is a factor of g (Lagrange's Theorem, p. 34). The question whether, conversely, G possesses at least one subgroup whose order is equal to a preassigned factor of g presents great difficulties, which have not yet been surmounted. To be sure, the case of cyclic groups is straightforward, and the answer is in the affirmative, as we saw in Chapter II, Theorem 4, p. 38. But where non-commutative groups are concerned, our knowledge is much more scanty.

We begin by proving a lemma which is a particular case of a theorem of A. Cauchy (see p. 129 below).

LEMMA 1. *If A is an Abelian group of order a and if p is any prime factor of a, then A contains at least one element of order p.*

Proof. The proposition is obviously true when $a = p$ (a prime number). We may therefore employ mathematical induction and shall henceforth assume that a is a composite number divisible by p. By Chapter II, Theorem 5, p. 40, A possesses proper subgroups. Let us select a *proper subgroup H of maximum order* h, $(h < a)$ say. We have to distinguish two cases :

(i) $p \mid h$. By induction, H contains an element $P(\neq I)$ such that $P^p = I$. Since P also belongs to A, this element satisfies our demands.

(ii) $(h, p) = 1$. Since H is a proper subgroup of A, there exists an element T of order t, say, which does not belong to H. Let $T(= \{T\})$ be the cyclic group generated by T and consider the product HT. Since A is Abelian, $HT = TH$ whence by the Product Theorem (p. 56), it follows that HT is a subgroup of A. It is obviously more comprehensive than H which, on the other hand, was supposed to be a maximal proper subgroup. Hence we must conclude that

$$A = HT.$$

The product on the right-hand side includes ht/d elements, where d is the order of $H \cap T$. Thus we obtain the relation

$$ad = ht.$$

The left-hand side is divisible by p. But since $(p, h) = 1$, it follows that $p \mid t$, i.e.

$$t = ps.$$

The element

$$P = T^s$$

is therefore of order p, as required.

40. Sylow's Theorems. Some remarkable results concerning subgroups of a certain type were discovered by the Norwegian mathematician L. Sylow.*

DEFINITION 1. *If the order of a group G is divisible by* p^m *but by no higher power of* p, *where* p *is a prime, then any subgroup of G of order* p^m *is called a* **Sylow group** *corresponding to* p.

THEOREM 1. *Every group of order g possesses at least one Sylow group corresponding to each prime factor of g.*

Proof. We shall again proceed by mathematical induction. The truth of the theorem is evident when $g = 2$ (the subgroup referred to need not be a proper subgroup). Let $g = p^m g'$, where $(g', p) = 1$. Resolving G into classes of conjugate elements (equation (4.4), p. 98), we have

$$G = (A_1) + (A_2) + \ldots + (A_k),$$

* " Théorèmes sur les groupes de substitutions ", *Math. Ann.* v (1872), p. 584.

and consequently

$$g = h_1 + h_2 + \ldots + h_k, \qquad . \qquad . \qquad . \quad (5.1)$$

where h_i is the number of elements in the class (A_i). It will be recalled that the normalizer of A_i is a group N_i whose order is given by

$$n_i = g/h_i \quad (i = 1, 2, \ldots, k) \qquad . \qquad . \quad (5.2)$$

(Chapter IV, Theorem 1, p. 97). We have to distinguish two cases :

(i) Suppose that one of the terms in (5.1), say h_l, is such that $h_l > 1$ and $(h_l, p) = 1$. It follows from (5.2) that n_l is less than g and is divisible by p^m (but by no higher power of p). Hence, by hypothesis, the theorem is true for N_l and we conclude that N_l possesses a subgroup of order p^m, which is of course also a subgroup of G and therefore a Sylow group corresponding to p.

(ii) Having disposed of case (i), we now assume that for every value of the suffix i in (5.1)

$$\text{either (a) } h_i = 1, \quad \text{or} \quad \text{(b) } p \mid h_i.$$

Terms of the type (a) correspond to self-conjugate elements, and we note that there is at least one such term, since I is a self-conjugate element. Denoting the exact number of self-conjugate elements (i.e. the order of the centre) by z (>0) and collecting in (5.1) all terms which are equal to 1, we obtain

$$p^m g' = z + xp,$$

whence

$$p \mid z.$$

Thus we see that the order of the centre is divisible by p. Since it is an Abelian group we learn from the lemma that G possesses at least one element P which commutes with all elements and is of order p, i.e. $X^{-1}PX = P$. The cyclic group

$$P = \{P\}$$

is therefore an invariant subgroup of G and G/P is of order

$p^{m-1}g'$. Hence, by the hypothesis of induction, G/P contains a Sylow group of order p^{m-1}. Such a subgroup can be written in the form H/P where H is a subgroup of G (Chapter IV, Theorem 10, p. 112) of order h, say. Thus we have

$$p^{m-1} = h/p,$$

i.e.

$$h = p^m.$$

The group H arrived at in this way is therefore a Sylow group of G corresponding to p.

As a corollary of this fundamental result we shall deduce Cauchy's theorem referred to at the beginning of this chapter.

THEOREM 2 (Cauchy).   *If* p *is a prime factor of the order of a group G, then G contains at least one element of order* p.

Proof.   Let H be a Sylow group of G of order p^m. If H is an element of H other than I, the order of H is of the form p^μ, where $\mu > 0$. Thus if we put

$$P = H^{p^{\mu-1}},$$

we have discovered an element of order p, since

$$P^p = H^{p^\mu} = I, \quad P \neq I.$$

It is quite possible that G may have more than one Sylow group of order p^m. Indeed, if A is one subgroup of this order, so is $X^{-1}AX$, where X is any element of G whatsoever (Chapter II, Theorem 2, p. 33), i.e. all groups conjugate with A are likewise Sylow groups. It might of course happen that some or all of these groups are identical with A. On the other hand, it will now be shown that we need not look for Sylow groups elsewhere.

THEOREM 3.   *All Sylow groups belonging to the same prime are conjugate to one another.*

Proof.   Let A and B be two subgroups of G of order p^m.

Decomposing G relative to A and B (equation (2.73), p. 59), we have

$$G = AP_1B + AP_2B + \ldots + AP_rB$$

and

$$g = \frac{ab}{d_1} + \frac{ab}{d_2} + \ldots + \frac{ab}{d_r}, \quad . \quad . \quad . \quad (5.3)$$

where d_ρ is the order of

$$D_\rho = P_\rho^{-1}AP_\rho \cap B. \quad . \quad . \quad . \quad (5.4)$$

In the present case $a = b = p^m$ and $g = p^m g'$, where $(g', p) = 1$. Hence, on dividing (5.3) throughout by p^m, we obtain

$$g' = \frac{p^m}{d_1} + \frac{p^m}{d_2} + \ldots + \frac{p^m}{d_r}. \quad . \quad . \quad (5.5)$$

Since D_ρ is a subgroup of B, its order, d_ρ, must be of the form p^μ $(0 \leqslant \mu \leqslant m)$, so that p^m/d_ρ is either a multiple of p, or else equal to unity. However, as the left-hand side of (5.5) is prime to p, not all terms on the right can be multiples of p, i.e. there exists at least one term, when $\rho = l$, say, such that

$$p^m/d_l = 1, \quad \text{i.e. } d_l = p^m.$$

Hence the corresponding group D_l is of the same order as B and since, by (5.4), it is contained in B, it follows that, in fact, $D_l = B$ and, for the same reason, $D_l = P_l^{-1}AP_l$. Hence

$$B = P_l^{-1}AP_l,$$

i.e. the two Sylow groups A and B are conjugate.

An interesting case arises when the Sylow group A is invariant in G, i.e. when it coincides with all its conjugate groups :

COROLLARY. *The Sylow group* A *is unique if, and only if, it is an invariant subgroup of* G.

A more precise statement regarding the number of Sylow groups is contained in the following :

THEOREM 4. *If there are exactly* k *Sylow groups of* G

corresponding to a prime p, *then* k *is an integer of the form*
$1 + \mathrm{p}x$ *and is a factor of the order of* G.

Proof. Theorem 3 implies that the number of distinct
Sylow groups is equal to the number k of distinct groups
conjugate with one of them.   Let A be a fixed Sylow group
corresponding to p and let N be the normalizer of A, i.e. the
set of all elements N of G such that

$$N^{-1}AN = A. \qquad . \qquad . \qquad . \qquad (5.6)$$

If N is of order n, we have

$$g = nk . \qquad . \qquad . \qquad . \qquad (5.7)$$

(Chapter IV, Theorem 3, p. 99), which shows that k is a
factor of g.   Since A is a group, each element A of A satisfies
the relation

$$A^{-1}AA = A$$

(Chapter II, Lemma 1, p. 32).   Hence A belongs to N ; and,
moreover, we infer from (5.6) that A is an invariant subgroup of N, i.e.

$$A \lessdot N. \qquad . \qquad . \qquad . \qquad (5.8)$$

Hence p^m, which is the order of A, is a factor of n so
that we may write

$$n = p^m n', \quad (n', p) = 1.$$

The last statement is justified because n, being a factor of g,
cannot be divisible by a power of p greater than p^m.

Let us now apply Frobenius' identity (Chapter II,
Theorem 8, p. 60) to the subgroups A and N of orders p^m
and n respectively, thus

$$G = AP_1N + AP_2N + \ldots + AP_rN \qquad . \qquad (5.9)$$

and

$$g = \frac{np^m}{d_1} + \frac{np^m}{d_2} + \ldots + \frac{np^m}{d_r}, \qquad . \qquad . \qquad (5.10)$$

where d_ρ is the order of

$$D_o = P_\rho^{-1}AP_\rho \cap N. \qquad . \qquad . \qquad (5.11)$$

K

There is no loss of generality in assuming that $P_1 = I$ and therefore

$$AP_1N = AIN = AN = N,$$

using (5.8) and the corollary on p. 32. The corresponding term in (5.10) is

$$\frac{np^m}{d_1} = n.$$

No other term in the expansion (5.9) is equal to N.

On dividing (5.10) throughout by n after substituting for g from (5.7), we get

$$k = 1 + \frac{p^m}{d_2} + \frac{p^m}{d_3} + \ldots + \frac{p^m}{d_r}. \qquad . \qquad . \quad (5.12)$$

Now D_ρ is a subgroup of $P_\rho{}^{-1}AP_\rho$ which, like A, is of order p^m. Hence it follows that p^m/d_ρ is of the form p^μ where $0 \leqslant \mu \leqslant m$. The essential step in the proof is to show that, except in the first term, μ is greater than 0, so that

$$k = 1 + xp. \qquad . \qquad . \qquad . \quad (5.13)$$

In order to arrive at this result, let us suppose that the λth term in (5.12) reduces to unity, i.e.

$$p^m = d_\lambda. \qquad . \qquad . \qquad . \quad (5.14)$$

By the same arguments as those which we used in the proof of Theorem 3 (p. 129), we come to the conclusion that $D_\lambda = P_\lambda{}^{-1}AP_\lambda$, i.e., since D_λ is a subgroup of N,

$$P_\lambda{}^{-1}AP_\lambda \subset N. \qquad . \qquad . \qquad . \quad (5.15)$$

We have seen that p^m is the highest power of p which divides the order of N. Thus N possesses one or more Sylow groups of order p^m. We have in fact found two such subgroups of N, namely A and $P_\lambda{}^{-1}AP_\lambda$. On the other hand, A is invariant in N and, by the Corollary on p. 130, is therefore unique, i.e. we must have

$$P_\lambda{}^{-1}AP_\lambda = A.$$

Remembering that N was defined as the normalizer of A, we infer that

$$P_\lambda \subset N, \quad P_\lambda N = N,$$

whence

$$AP_\lambda N = AN = N.$$

However, this equation is impossible unless $\lambda = 1$. Hence all terms of (5.12) except the first are divisible by p, which at once leads to (5.13). This completes the proof of the theorem.

As an application we shall prove the following :

THEOREM 5.   *Any group G whose order is of the form* pq, *where* p *and* q *are primes such that* $p \not\equiv 1$ (mod. q) *and* $q \not\equiv 1$ (mod. p), *is necessarily an Abelian group.*

Proof. The case in which $p = q$ having already been dealt with (Chapter IV, Theorem 5, p. 104), we shall assume that $(p, q) = 1$. Let $P (= \{P\})$ be a Sylow group of G corresponding to p. We know that the number of such subgroups is a divisor of pq and is of the form $1 + px$. Since $q \not\equiv 1$ (mod. p), it is necessarily equal to 1, the other factors of pq, namely p, q and pq, being incompatible with the conditions. Thus by the Corollary on p. 130 P is an invariant subgroup of G of order p. Similarly $Q (= \{Q\})$ is an invariant subgroup of order q. Hence we have

$$PQ = QP$$

(see equation (4.8)), and by the Product Theorem (p. 56) the product of these two complexes represents a group of order pq/d, where d is the order of $P \cap Q$. Since $(p, q) = 1$, the two groups can have only the unit element in common, i.e. $d = 1$ and therefore

$$G = PQ.$$

Again, by Chapter IV, Theorem 7, p. 106, every element of P commutes with every element of Q ; in particular

$$PQ = QP.$$

Thus the pq elements of G can be written

$$P^\alpha Q^\beta \quad \text{or} \quad Q^\beta P^\alpha \quad (\alpha = 0, 1, \ldots, p-1 ; \quad \beta = 0, 1, \ldots, q-1),$$

which evidently defines an Abelian group.

41. Prime Power Groups. This is the name given to groups of order p^m, where p is a prime. All Sylow groups are of this type. Prime power groups possess a number of interesting properties, one of which we encountered in Chapter IV, Theorem 2, p. 99, where we saw that a group G of order p^m always contains at least one invariant element P of order p. We have then

$$X^{-1}PX = P,$$

where X is any element of G, and *the cyclic group*

$$P = \{P\}$$

is an invariant subgroup of order p. This result may be generalized as follows :

THEOREM 6. *A group of order* p^m *possesses at least one invariant subgroup of order* p^μ, *where* $0 < \mu < \mathrm{m}$.

Proof. The theorem is true when $m = 2$, since in that case the group is Abelian (Chapter IV, Theorem 5, p. 104), and any element of order p generates an invariant subgroup of order p. Thus we have a basis for induction. Let G be a group of order p^m $(m > 2)$. Let P be an invariant subgroup of G of order p. The quotient group G/P is of order p^{m-1}. We may therefore assume that G/P has an invariant subgroup of order $p^{\mu-1}$. Such a group can be written in the form

$$A/P,$$

where A is an invariant subgroup of G, which must evidently be of order p^μ. (Chapter IV, Theorem 10, p. 111.)

COROLLARY. *All prime power groups are soluble.*

For a group G of order p^m possesses an invariant subgroup A_1 of order p^{m-1}, which in turn contains an invariant subgroup of order p^{m-2}, etc. Thus we can construct a composition series

$$G \succ A_1 \succ A_2 \succ \ldots \succ A_{m-1} \succ I,$$

in which all composition indices are equal to p.

Example 1. *There can be no simple group of order 200.*
For since $200 = 5^2 \times 8$, the group contains k Sylow groups of
order 25, where k is of the form $1 + 5x$ ($x = 0, 1, 2, \ldots$) and
a divisor of 200. Since $(k, 5) = 1$, we must have $k \mid 8$,
which is impossible unless $x = 0$, i.e. there is a unique
invariant Sylow group of order 25. Thus the group is not
simple.

Example 2. *There can be no simple group of order 30.*
For if there were such a group, none of its Sylow groups
would be unique. Hence it would have $1 + 5 (= 6)$ Sylow
groups of order 5 comprising $6 \times 4 (= 24)$ elements of
order 5. Also there would be $1 + 3 \times 3 (= 10)$ Sylow groups
of order 3, and so the total number of elements would
exceed 30.

Examples

(1) Show that A_4 has one Sylow group of order 4 and four
Sylow groups of order 3.

(2) Prove that there is no simple group of order 56.

(3) If G is a group of order p^2q, where p and q are primes
such that q is less than p and not a factor of $p^2 - 1$, prove that
G is Abelian.

(4) Prove that any subgroup whose order is a power of p
(a prime factor of g) is contained in at least one of the Sylow
groups corresponding to p.

(5) Show that an invariant subgroup whose order is a
power of p is contained in every Sylow group corresponding to p.

(6) If every Sylow group of G is an invariant subgroup,
show that G is the direct product of its Sylow groups.

HINTS and ANSWERS. 2. Otherwise there would be eight
Sylow groups of order 7 and seven of order 8. 3. Prove that both
Sylow groups are unique and use Chapter IV, Theorem 7, p. 106.
4. Apply the expansion (Chapter II, Theorem 8, p. 60) to this
subgroup and to a Sylow group. 5. Consider the subgroup
generated by the subgroup and a Sylow group. 6. Use Chapter
IV, Theorem 7, p. 106.

CHAPTER VI

ABELIAN GROUPS

42. Additive Notation. When the composition of group elements is commutative, i.e. when the group is Abelian, it is often convenient to write the composite C of two elements A and B as their sum rather than their product, thus

$$C = A + B = B + A. \qquad . \qquad . \qquad . \quad (6.1)$$

For example, the ordinary integers form such a group relative to addition. Another instance was mentioned in Example 2 on p. 25. The validity of (6.1) will be assumed throughout this chapter.

In adopting the additive notation we are of course compelled to discontinue the use of the " + " sign ((2.2), p. 28) for gathering elements into a complex. From now on the elements of a complex will simply be enumerated thus

$$K: A, B, C, \ldots$$

Instead of a unit element it is now more natural to speak of a *zero element* or *neutral element*, which we write as 0 and which has the property that, for every A,

$$A + 0 = 0 + A = A.$$

It is the only group element satisfying the equation

$$X + X = X.$$

The inverse of A is now expressed as $-A$, and we have

$$A + (-A) = (-A) + A = 0.$$

Generally, $A + (-B)$ and $0 + (-B)$ are contracted to $A - B$

and $-B$ respectively. Instead of the successive powers of a simple element we now have

$$A + A = 2A,$$
$$A + A + A = 3A, \ldots$$

etc., where kA is to be regarded as an abbreviation for a sum of k terms each equal to A. It is natural to introduce the notation $-kA$ for $-(kA)$. Evidently

$$(k + l)A = kA + lA$$

for any integers k, l. Furthermore, in virtue of (6.1) we have

$$2(A + B) = A + B + A + B = 2A + 2B$$

and, more generally, for any integer k,

$$k(A + B) = kA + kB. \qquad . \qquad . \qquad . \qquad (6.2)$$

It is this relation which makes the study of Abelian groups so much simpler than that of non-commutative groups.

The order of an element A is the least positive integer m such that

$$mA = 0.$$

Such an element generates a cyclic group

$$0, A, 2A, \ldots, (m-1)A$$

of order m. If

$$nA = 0,$$

where n is a positive integer, then n is a multiple of m. It is clear how the group axioms (pp. 2-3) have to be adapted to the additive notation. We observe that a non-empty complex K of G forms a subgroup if, and only if, $A - B$ belongs to K whenever A and B do. For on first letting $A = B$ and then $A = 0, B = A$, we deduce that K contains the elements 0 and $-A$. The associative law holds in K since it holds in G.

Let

$$A : 0, A_2, \ldots, A_a$$

be a subgroup of order a of G. Then G can be resolved into cosets relative to A, thus

$$G : A + 0, \; A + U_2, \ldots, A + U_n, \qquad . \qquad . \quad (6.3)$$

where n is the index of A in G. A typical coset $A + U$ consists of a elements, namely

$$A + U : U, \; A_2 + U, \ldots, A_a + U.$$

Two cosets $A + X$ and $A + Y$ are equal if, and only if, $X - Y$ belongs to A. In view of the commutative law we need not distinguish between right and left cosets. Also, as in Chapter II, we shall agree to disregard duplicates amongst the elements of a complex, and in particular we have, for a subgroup A,

$$A + A = A. \qquad . \qquad . \qquad . \qquad . \quad (6.4)$$

In Abelian groups all subgroups are invariant and the cosets may be regarded as elements of a group

$$G - A,$$

which is called the **difference group** of G relative to A. The composition of its elements follows the pattern

$$(A + X) + (A + Y) = A + X + Y.$$

The zero element of $G - A$ is A and the inverse of $A + X$ is $A - X$. Briefly, one passes from G to $G - A$ by reducing the elements of G mod. A. This process is analogous to the way in which classes of residues are formed relative to a fixed integer m (p. 15). The group A in this case is infinite and consists of all integral multiples of m, i.e.

$$A : 0, \; \pm \, m, \; \pm \, 2m, \ldots$$

while G is the additive group of all integers. The difference group $G - A$ is of order m and consists of the elements

$$A + 0, \; A + 1, \ldots, \; A + (m - 1).$$

If K and L are complexes of a group G, the complex $K + L$

is the collection of all elements of the form $X + Y$ where $X \subset K$ and $Y \subset L$. Since the group is Abelian,

$$K + L = L + K.$$

Let U and V be any subgroups of G, then $U + V$ is also a subgroup because (see (6.4))

$$(U + V) + (U + V) = U + U + V + V = U + V.$$

Thus the Product Theorem (p. 56) becomes trivial in the case of Abelian groups.

It may happen that the subgroups U and V generate the whole of G, so that

$$G = U + V. \qquad . \qquad . \qquad . \qquad (6.5)$$

We are especially interested in the particular case when U and V have only the zero element in common.

DEFINITION 1. *A group G is said to be the* **direct sum** *of two subgroups U and V if every element X of G can be expressed in the form $X = U + V$ where $U \subset U$ and $V \subset V$, and if $U + V = 0$ implies that $U = V = 0$. We shall write the direct sum as*

$$G = U \oplus V. \qquad . \qquad . \qquad . \qquad (6.6)$$

It is clear that under these conditions U and V cannot have a non-zero element W in common, or else

$$W + (-W) = 0 \quad (W \subset U, \ -W \subset V)$$

would be a non-trivial decomposition of 0. Also, the components U and V of X are uniquely determined by X, since

$$X = U_1 + V_1 = U_2 + V_2$$

would imply that

$$U_1 - U_2 = V_2 - V_1 = W,$$

which would be an element of $U \cap V$ and hence is zero.

More generally, we have

$$G = U_1 \oplus U_2 \oplus \ldots \oplus U_r, \qquad . \qquad . \qquad (6.7)$$

if every element X of G can be expressed as

$$X = U_1 + U_2 + \ldots + U_r, \quad (U_i \subset U_i) \qquad (6.8)$$

and if

$$0 = U_1 + U_2 + \ldots + U_r \quad . \quad . \quad . \quad (6.9)$$

implies that

$$U_i = 0 \quad (i = 1, 2, \ldots, r).$$

The order of G is then given by

$$g = u_1 u_2 \ldots u_r,$$

where u_r is the order of U_r.

Alternatively, we can say that G is the direct sum of the subgroups $U_1, U_2, \ldots, U_r$ if, and only if, every element X of G possesses a unique expansion of the form (6.8). For suppose a certain element X has two such expansions, say

$$X = U_1 + U_2 + \ldots U_r = U'_1 + U'_2 + \ldots + U'_r$$

so that

$$0 = (U_1 - U'_1) + (U_2 - U'_2) + \ldots + (U_r - U'_r).$$

As in (6.9) it then follows that $U_i - U'_i = 0$ $(i = 1, 2, \ldots, r)$.

Finally, we remark that the process of splitting an Abelian group into a direct sum of subgroups may be carried out in successive stages, thus if

$$G = U \oplus V, \quad V = X \oplus Y,$$

we have

$$G = U \oplus X \oplus Y.$$

43. The Basis Theorem for finite Abelian Group.

In the next two sections we discuss the problem of decomposing an Abelian group into the direct sum of cyclic groups. Suppose G is of order

$$g = p^a q^b r^c \ldots, \quad . \quad . \quad . \quad (6.10)$$

where p, q, r, . . . are distinct primes. The collection of elements of G whose order is a power of p, forms a subgroup P, for if $p^m X = 0$ and $p^n Y = 0$ where $n \geqslant m$, say, we have

$$p^n(X + Y) = p^n X + p^n Y = 0$$

so that $X + Y$ belongs to P. Also $-X$ belongs to P and so does 0, whose order is $1(=p^0)$. Similarly, we define groups Q, R, . . . as the aggregates of all elements whose orders are powers of q, r . . . respectively. Let X be any element of G of order

$$f = p^\alpha q^\beta r^\gamma \ldots = p^\alpha f_1$$

where α, β, γ . . ., are non-negative integers. Using Theorem 4 of § 8 in the additive notation, we can write

$$X = P + X_1,$$

where P and X_1 are of orders p^α and f_1 respectively. On repeating this argument we finally obtain a decomposition

$$X = P + Q + R + \ldots \quad . \quad . \quad . \quad (6.11)$$

where $P \subset P, Q \subset Q, R \subset R, \ldots$. In order to show that the representation is unique suppose that

$$0 = P_0 + Q_0 + R_0 + \ldots \quad . \quad . \quad . \quad (6.12)$$

where $P_0 \subset R, Q_0 \subset Q, R_0 \subset R$. On transposing the first term we see that the order of P_0 is a power of p and a factor of $q^b r^c \ldots$, which is impossible unless the order is 1, i.e. $P_0 = 0$. Similarly, it is shown that $Q_0 = R_0 = \ldots = 0$. Thus we have

THEOREM 1. *If* G *is an Abelian group of order* g $= p^a q^b r^c$ . . ., *then*

$$G = P \oplus Q \oplus R \oplus \ldots, \quad . \quad . \quad . \quad (6.13)$$

where P, Q, R, . . . *are the collections of elements whose orders are powers of* p, q, r, . . . *respectively.*

Before continuing our investigations it will be convenient to introduce the following concept.

DEFINITION 2. *If in an Abelian group* G *there are elements* $A_1, A_2, \ldots, A_q$ *of orders* $m_1, m_2, \ldots, m_q$ *respectively, such that every element* X *of* G *can be uniquely represented in the form*

$$X = x_1 A_1 + x_2 A_2 + \ldots + x_q A_q$$

where $0 \leqslant x_i < m_i (i = 1, 2, \ldots q)$ *then* A_1, A_2, ..., A_q *are called a* **basis** *of* G.

In every Abelian group with a finite number of generators

$$G_1, G_2, \ldots, G_k$$

(see p. 42) an arbitrary element Y can be written as

$$Y = y_1 G_1 + y_2 G_2 + \ldots + y_k G_k, \qquad . \qquad . \quad (6.14)$$

because, in virtue of the commutative law, terms in $G_i (i = 1, 2, \ldots k)$ may be gathered into a single term. Thus a set of generators constitutes a basis if, and only if, the representation (6.14) is unique for each Y.

The existence of a basis is equivalent to saying that

$$G = \{A_1\} \oplus \{A_2\} \oplus \ldots \oplus \{A_q\}, \ldots \qquad . \quad (6.15)$$

where $\{A\}$ denotes the cyclic group generated by A. Thus if G is the direct sum of cyclic groups, as in (6.15), every element X of G can be expressed as

$$X = x_1 A_1 + \ldots + x_q A_q \quad (0 \leqslant x_i < m_i),$$

and an equation of the form

$$c_1 A_1 + \ldots + c_q A_q = 0$$

implies that each term vanishes, i.e. that c_i is a (zero or non-zero) multiple of the order of A_i.

THEOREM 2. (Basis Theorem for finite Abelian groups.)[*]
Every finite Abelian group is the direct sum of cyclic groups of prime power order.

Proof. In view of Theorem 1 it is sufficient to prove this theorem for a group in which the order of every element is a power of a fixed prime p, and we shall accordingly

---

[*] G. A. Miller suggests that this theorem be regarded as the fourth in order of importance, being preceded only by the theorems of Lagrange (p. 34), Sylow (p. 127) and Cayley (p. 80), see G. A. Miller, H. F. Blichfeldt and L. E. Dickson, *Theory and Application of Finite Groups* (New York, 1916).

assume that P is a finite Abelian group with this property.

Let A_1 be an element of maximal order p^{m_1}, say. Let

$$P_1 = \{A_1\}$$

be the cyclic group of order p^{m_1} generated by A_1. Hence an equation

$$x_1 A_1 = 0$$

is impossible, unless x_1 is a multiple of p^{m_1}.

It may happen that $P = P_1$. In that case P is cyclic and there is nothing further to prove. If, however, $P_1 \neq P$, the proof may be completed by induction as follows.

Suppose we have found k elements

$$A_1, A_2, \ldots, A_k \qquad . \qquad . \qquad . \quad (6.16)$$

of orders

$$p^{m_1}, p^{m_2}, \ldots, p^{m_k} \qquad . \qquad . \qquad . \quad (6.17)$$

such that

(i) the set of orders is maximal in the sense that

$$m_1 \geqslant m_2 \geqslant \ldots \geqslant m_k,$$

and any further element of P is of order p^μ where

$$\mu \leqslant m_k,$$

(ii) a relation of the form

$$c_1 A_1 + c_2 A_2 + \ldots + c_k A_k = 0$$

implies that each term vanishes, i.e. that

$$c_i = c_i' p^{m_i} \quad (i = 1, 2, \ldots, k).$$

The subgroup P_k generated by the elements (6.16) is therefore a direct sum, thus

$$P_k = \{A_1\} \oplus \{A_2\} \oplus \ldots \oplus \{A_k\}. \qquad . \qquad . \quad (6.18)$$

If P_k is not the whole of P, let B be an element not in P_k. This does not exclude the possibility that a certain multiple of B lies in P_k; in fact, if p^μ is the order of B, we certainly have $p^\mu B = 0 \subset P_k$. Suppose then that vB is the least positive multiple of B to lie in P_k. Then

$$vB = \sum_{i=1}^{k} y_i A_i, \ v \leqslant p^\mu. \quad . \quad . \quad . \quad (6.19)$$

First of all we show that v is a power of p; for on dividing p^μ by v we have

$$p^\mu = sv + t, \quad (0 \leqslant t < v)$$

whence we deduce that tB lies in P_k because $p^\mu B$ and $s(vB)$ do. The minimal property of v then implies that $t = 0$. Thus v is a factor of p^μ and must therefore be a power of p, say

$$v = p^{m_{k+1}}, \quad . \quad . \quad . \quad (6.20)$$

where $m_{k+1} \leqslant \mu$, and hence by (i)

$$m_{k+1} \leqslant m_k \leqslant \ldots \leqslant m_2 \leqslant m_1. \quad . \quad (6.21)$$

Next we prove that each coefficient y_i in (6.19) is divisible by v. For on multiplying (6.19) by p^μ/v we obtain

$$p^\mu B = 0 = \sum_{i=1}^{k} (y_i p^\mu/v) A_i,$$

whence by (ii)

$$y_i p^\mu/v = y_i' p^{m_i} (i = 1, 2, \ldots, k).$$

This relation may be written

$$y_i = v y_i' p^{m_i - \mu} = v z_i, \quad . \quad . \quad . \quad (6.22)$$

where $z_i = y_i' p^{m_i - \mu}$ is an integer because $\mu \leqslant m_i$. We now define

$$A_{k+1} = B - \sum_{i=1}^{k} z_i A_i.$$

The order of A_{k+1} is v. For, by (6.19) and (6.22), $vA_{k+1} = 0$ and any other equation of the form $uA_{k+1} = 0$, where $u > 0$ implies that $uB \subset P_k$ and hence $u \geqslant v$. Next, we shall prove that if

$$c_1 A_1 + \ldots + c_k A_k + c_{k+1} A_{k+1} = 0, \quad . \quad (6.23)$$

then c_i is divisible by $p^{m_i} (i=1, 2, \ldots, k+1)$. For we infer from (6.23) that $c_{k+1}A_{k+1}$ lies in P_k and hence so does $c_{k+1}B$. On dividing c_{k+1} by v we deduce from the minimal property of v (as above) that c_{k+1} is in fact divisible by v. Thus

$$c_{k+1} = p^{m_{k+1}}c_{k}{'}_{+1}.$$

The last term on the left of (23) is therefore zero, and the equations

$$c_i = p^{m_i}c_i{'} (i=1, 2, \ldots k)$$

follow from property (ii).

Thus if $P_k \neq P$ we can add an element A_{k+1} to the set (6.16) which will then have the properties (i) and (ii) with $k+1$ instead of k. It is evident how the proof of the theorem is to be completed. Starting from an element A_1 of maximal order ($k=1$), we can find further elements satisfying (i) and (ii) until the whole group is exhausted.

If this happens at the sth step we obtain

$$P = \{A_1\} \oplus \{A_2\} \oplus \ldots \oplus \{A_s\}, \qquad . \qquad . \quad (6.24)$$

so that P is expressed as the direct sum of s cyclic groups of orders

$$p^{m_1} \geqslant p^{m_2} \geqslant \ldots \geqslant p^{m_s} \qquad . \qquad . \quad (6.25)$$

respectively. This concludes the proof of the theorem.

We remark that the order of P is now seen to be p^a, where $a = m_1 + m_2 + \ldots + m_s$. Thus we have proved incidentally that if the order of each element of an Abelian group is a power of a fixed prime, the order of the whole group is a power of that prime. It was shown in Theorem 2 (p. 129) of the preceding chapter that this fact is true even for non-Abelian groups.

In accordance with the definition 1 of § 40, p. 127, we shall refer to the groups $P, Q, R \ldots$ of Theorem 1 as the Sylow Groups of G corresponding to the primes $p, q, r \ldots$ respectively. If G is of order

$$g = p^a q^b r^c \ldots$$

the Sylow groups, which are uniquely determined by G, are of orders p^a, q^b, r^c, . . . respectively.

COROLLARY 1. *In a finite Abelian group the order of any element is a factor of the maximal order ; i.e. there exists an element of order* h *such that every group element satisfies the equation* $hX = 0$.

Proof. The proposition is certainly true for an Abelian group of prime power order (see 6.25). In the case of an Abelian group of composite order we make use of the decomposition

$$G = P \oplus Q \oplus \ . \ . \ .$$

If P, Q . . . are elements of maximal orders p^m, q^n . . . in the groups P, Q, . . . respectively, then

$$M = P + Q + \ . \ . \ .$$

is an element of maximal order $h = p^m q^n$ . . . in G.

COROLLARY 2. *If* $C(g)$ *is a cyclic group of order*

$$g = p^a q^b r^c \ . \ . \ .$$

then

$$C(g) = C(p^a) \oplus C(q^b) \oplus C(r^c) \oplus. \ . \ . \ .$$

For the Sylow groups of $C(g)$, being subgroups of a cyclic group, are themselves cyclic groups.

44. Elementary Divisors and Invariants of a finite Abelian Group. It is clear that the basis elements of an Abelian group G are by no means uniquely determined. Indeed such is not even the case when the group itself is cyclic of order greater than 2. On the other hand, since cyclic groups of equal order are isomorphic, the structure of G is determined by the orders of its cyclic components. That these orders are, conversely, determined by the group itself, is asserted by the following theorem.

THEOREM 3. *If a finite Abelian group* G *has been decomposed into the direct sum of cyclic groups of prime power orders, these orders are called the* **elementary divisors** *of* G. *They are completely determined by the group itself. Thus if*

$$G = \{A_1\} \oplus \{A_2\} \oplus. \ . \ . \oplus \{A_u\} \qquad . \qquad . \quad (6.26)$$

and

$$G = \{B_1\} \oplus \{B_2\} \oplus \ldots \oplus \{B_v\}, \quad . \quad . \quad (6.27)$$

where the order of each A *and* B *is a power of some prime, then* u = v *and the orders in* (6.26) *and* (6.27) *are equal in pairs.*

Proof. It is sufficient to prove the theorem for groups of prime power order, since in the notation of Theorem 1 (p. 14) the elementary divisors of G are those of its Sylow groups P, Q, R, . . . taken together.

Suppose then that

$$P = \{P_1\} \oplus \{P_2\} \oplus \ldots \oplus \{P_t\} \quad . \quad . \quad (6.28)$$

is an Abelian group of order p^a, decomposed into the direct sum of cyclic group of orders

$$p^{m_1} \geqslant p^{m_2} \geqslant \ldots \geqslant p^{m_t}. \quad . \quad . \quad (6.29)$$

These are the elementary divisors of P. For our purpose it is more convenient to describe the set (6.28) as consisting of the powers p, p^2, p^3 . . . with multiplicities a_1, a_2, a_3 . . . where $a_i \geqslant 0$. The invariance of the a's will be established if we can express them in terms of numbers which are determined by the group P itself, without reference to a basis.* Such quantities are furnished by any one of the equations

$$p^k X = 0. \quad (k = 0, 1, 2, \ldots). \quad . \quad . \quad (6.30)$$

It is clear that the number, c_k say, of group elements satisfying (6.30) for a particular value of k is a property of the group alone and does not depend on the decomposition (6.28). (Evidently $c_0 = 1$.) It therefore suffices to prove that the a's can be expressed in terms of the c's. In fact, we shall show that

$$p^{a_k} = \frac{c_k{}^2}{c_{k+1} c_{k-1}} \quad (k = 1, 2, \ldots). \quad . \quad . \quad (6.31)$$

Consider first the case where P = {P} is a cyclic group of

* See G. Pickert, *Einführung in die Höhere Algebra* (Göttingen, 1951), 152.

L

order p^h, and let $\psi(h, k)$ denote the number of solutions of (6.30), which in the present case reduces to

$$p^k x P = 0 \quad (0 \leqslant x < p^h). \quad . \quad . \quad . \quad (6.32)$$

If $k \geqslant h$, (6.32) is true for all x, since $p^h P = 0$. But if $k \leqslant h$, x must be of the form $p^{h-k}y$ where y can be chosen in p^k different ways. Hence

$$\psi(h, k) = \begin{cases} p^h \text{ if } k \geqslant h \\ p^k \text{ if } k \leqslant h, \end{cases} \quad . \quad . \quad (6.33)$$

and a simple calculation yields the result

$$\frac{\{\psi(h, k)\}^2}{\psi(h, k+1)\psi(h, k-1)} = \begin{cases} 1 \text{ if } h > k \text{ or } h < k \\ p \text{ if } h = k \end{cases} \quad . \quad . \quad (6.34)$$

Turning now to the group given in (6.28), we note that a typical element is of the form

$$X = x_1 P_1 + x_2 P_2 + \ldots + x_t P_t.$$

Since the sum is direct, X is a solution of (6.30) if, and only if,

$$p^k x_j P_j = 0 \quad (j = 1, \ 2, \ldots, t). \quad . \quad . \quad (6.35)$$

These t equations are independent of one another, and since the jth equation has $\psi(m_j, k)$ solutions, it follows that the number of solutions of (6.30) is

$$c_k = \prod_{j=1}^{t} \psi(m_j, k) \quad (k = 0, 1, 2 \ldots). \quad . \quad (6.36)$$

On using (6.34) we find that

$$\frac{c_k{}^2}{c_{k+1}c_{k-1}} = \prod_{j=1}^{t} \frac{\{\psi(m_j, k)\}^2}{\psi(m_j, k+1)\psi(m_j, k-1)} = p^{\alpha_k}$$

$(k = 1, 2, \ldots)$. This establishes (6.31) and hence proves the theorem.

DEFINITION 3. *An Abelian group of order* p^m *is said to be of* **type** $(m_1, m_2, \ldots, m_k)$ *if it is the direct sum of cyclic groups of orders*

$$p^{m_1}, p^{m_2}, \ldots, p^{m_k} \quad . \quad . \quad . \quad (6.37)$$

where

$$m_1 \geqslant m_2 \geqslant \ldots \geqslant m_k > 0 \quad m_1 + m_2 + \ldots + m_k = m, \quad . \quad (6.38)$$

i.e. if (6.37) *are the elementary divisors of the group.*

Thus there are as many different Abelian groups of order p^m as there are partitions of m satisfying (6.38). E.g., there are three Abelian groups of order $8(=2^3)$ corresponding to the types (3), (2, 1), (1, 1, 1) respectively (see Chapter II, p. 51).

Returning to the case of an arbitrary Abelian group of finite order

$$g = p^a q^b r^c \ldots$$

let the elementary divisors of the Sylow groups be arranged in an array

$$\left.\begin{array}{ll} p^{a_1}, p^{a_2}, \ldots & (a_1 \geqslant a_2 \geqslant \ldots, \; a_1 + a_2 + \ldots = a) \\ q^{b_1}, q^{b_2}, \ldots & (b_1 \geqslant b_2 \geqslant \ldots, \; b_1 + b_2 + \ldots = b) \\ r^{c_1}, r^{c_2}, \ldots & (c_1 \geqslant c_2 \geqslant \ldots, \; c_1 + c_2 + \ldots = c) \end{array}\right\} \quad (6.39)$$

where each row contains the elementary divisors of a Sylow group, and G is the direct sum of all the cyclic groups whose orders are listed in (6.39). It is impossible to carry the decomposition of G into cyclic groups any further, and in that respect the elementary divisors of an Abelian group correspond to its ultimate constituents.

On the other hand, if it desired only to decompose G into cyclic groups, whether of prime power order or not, the number of direct summands can, in general, be reduced by making use of Corollary 2, p. 146. For we may gather into a single cylic group all those cyclic groups whose orders occupy the first column of (6.39), thus

$$C(n_1) = C(p^{a_1}) \oplus C(q^{b_1}) \oplus C(r^{c_1}) \oplus \; \ldots \; (n_1 = p^{a_1} q_{b_1} r^{c_1} \ldots).$$

Similarly,

$$C(n_2) = C(p^{a_2}) \oplus C(q^{b_2}) \oplus C(r^{c_2}) \oplus \; \ldots \; (n_2 = p^{a_2} q^{b_2} r^{c_2} \ldots)$$

etc. Since $a_1 \geqslant a_2$, $b_1 \geqslant b_2$, $c_1 \geqslant c_2$, $\ldots$ we have $n_2 | n_1$, and generally $n_i | n_{i-1}$ ($i = 2, 3, \ldots$).

DEFINITION 4. *The integers* n_1, n_2, . . . *obtained by forming the products of the prime powers in each column of the array of elementary divisors are called the* **invariants** * *of* G. *They are characterized by the following properties*

(i) $G = C(n_1) \oplus C(n_2) \oplus C(n_3) \oplus$ . . .
(ii) $n_i | n_{i-1}$ $(i = 2, 3, . . .)$

The invariants are uniquely determined by the elementary divisors and, conversely, if we resolve each invariant into prime factors, we recover the array of elementary divisors. Hence a complete picture of the group structure can be obtained either from the elementary divisors or from the invariants.

Example. Find the elementary divisors and invariants of the Abelian group defined by

$$30A = 12B = 0.$$

This group is of order $30 \times 12 = 360 = 8 \times 9 \times 5$. Its Sylow groups are therefore of orders 8, 9, 5 respectively, and can be expressed in terms of the generators as follows :

$\{3B, 15A\}$ of order 8 and elementary divisors (4, 2)
$\{10A, 4B\}$ of order 9 and elementary divisors (3, 3)
$\{6A\}$ of order 5 and elementary divisor (5).

The invariants are accordingly

$$n_1 = 4 \times 3 \times 5 = 60, \quad n_2 = 2 \times 3 = 6.$$

45. Finitely Generated Infinite Abelian Groups. The results of the preceding sections imply that the structure of a finite Abelian group is clearly exhibited as soon as the group has been resolved into the direct sum of cyclic groups, i.e. as soon as a basis has been found. We shall now show that similar circumstances prevail even in the case of infinite Abelian groups if they are finitely generated. The simplest type of infinite Abelian group is an infinite

* Or **torsion coefficients** (on account of their significance in topology).

cyclic group. It has a single generator, A, and consists of the elements

$$0, \pm A, \pm 2A, \ldots, \pm nA, \ldots$$

If the Abelian group G is generated by $A_1, A_2, \ldots, A_n$, every element can be written in the form

$$X = x_1 A_1 + x_2 A_2 + \ldots + x_n A_n, \quad . \quad . \quad (6.40)$$

where the x_i are positive or negative integers.

In order to simplify the discussion we confine ourselves to **irredundant** sets of generators, that is, we assume that no generator can be expressed in terms of the others. In particular, zero will not be one of the generators. (We may evidently exclude the case in which G consists of the zero element only.) Nevertheless, even in an irredundant set the generators may be related by an equation of the form

$$b_1 A_1 + b_2 A_2 + \ldots + b_n A_n = 0,$$

in which no b is 1 or -1. For such an equation cannot be used to eliminate one of the A's, since fractional coefficients are, of course, inadmissible.

We begin by considering the special case of a group in which every non-zero element is of infinite order. Such groups are called **locally infinite**.

THEOREM 4. *A finitely generated locally infinite Abelian group G is the direct sum of a finite number of infinite cyclic groups, i.e. there exist r elements $C_1, C_r, \ldots, C_r$ such that every element X of G can be uniquely expressed in the form*

$$X = x_1 C_1 + x_2 C_2 + \ldots + x_r C_r$$

with integral coefficients ; or, equivalently,

$$G = \{C_1\} \oplus \{C_2\} \oplus \ldots \oplus \{C_r\}.$$

The number r, *which is called the* **rank** *of* G, *is uniquely determined.*

N.B. A group of this kind is said to be **free Abelian**, and the basis elements C_1, C_2, . . ., C_r are called **free generators**, because they are not constrained by any equation of the form $x_1 C_1 + x_2 C_2 + . . . + x_r C_r = 0$, with some x's non-zero. Our theorem then asserts that *a finitely generated locally infinite Abelian group is necessarily free.*

Proof. Suppose the theorem were false. The group, though finitely generated, would then have no set of free generators. Hence every set of generators A_1, A_2 . . ., A_n satisfies at least one equation of the form

$$b_1 A_1 + b_2 A_2 + . . . + b_n A_n = 0,$$

where

$$h = |b_1| + |b_2| + . . . + |b_n|$$

is a positive integer, which we call the **height** of the relation. From all possible irredundant sets of generators select one, say, Q_1, Q_2, . . ., Q_m, whose relations include one of minimum height. Let this particular relation be

$$u_1 Q_1 + u_2 Q_2 + . . . + u_m Q_m = 0 \qquad . \qquad (6.41)$$

and denote its height by

$$h_0 = |u_1| + |u_2| + . . . + |u_m|.$$

We may then assert that if

$$t_1 B_1 + t_2 B_2 + . . . + t_l B_l = 0$$

is any non-trivial relation between a set of generators B_1, B_2, . . ., B_l, then

$$|t_1| + |t_2| + . . . + |t_l| \geqslant h_0.$$

We observe that at least two coefficients in (6.41) are non-zero, because an equation of the form $uQ = 0$ ($Q \neq 0$) contradicts the hypothesis that the group has no elements of finite order. Suppose then that

$$|u_1| \geqslant |u_2| > 0,$$

and write

$$u_1 = qu_2 + u_1'$$

where

$$|u_1'| < |u_2| \leqslant |u_1|.$$

Substituting for u_1 in (6.41), we obtain

$$u_1'Q_1 + u_2(Q_2 + qQ_1) + u_3Q_3 + \ldots + u_mQ_m = 0.$$

Now $Q_2 + qQ_1 \neq 0$, since the Q's form an irredundant set of generators, and

$$Q_1' = Q_1, \quad Q_2' = Q_2 + qQ_1, \quad Q_3' = Q_3, \ldots, Q_m' = Q_m$$

also generate the group, since conversely each Q can be expressed in terms of the Q'. The generators Q' are irredundant and satisfy the equation

$$u_1'Q_1' + u_2Q_2' + \ldots + u_mQ_m' = 0, \qquad . \quad (6.42)$$

where

$$0 < |u_1'| + |u_2| + \ldots + |u_m| < h_0.$$

This contradicts the minimal property of h_0. It follows that the group must, after all, have a set of free generators, say, $C_1, C_2, \ldots, C_r$. Thus

$$\mathbf{G} = \{C_1\} \oplus \{C_2\} \oplus \ldots \oplus \{C_r\}.$$

In order to prove the uniqueness of r, suppose that

$$\mathbf{G} = \{D_1\} \oplus \{D_2\} \oplus \ldots \oplus \{D_s\}, \qquad . \quad (6.43)$$

where $s > r$ say. Each D must be expressible in terms of the C's, thus

$$D_i = \sum_{j=1}^{r} a_{ij}C_j \ (i = 1, 2, \ldots s), \qquad . \quad . \quad (6.44)$$

where a_{ij} is an integer. From the theory of linear equations * it follows that the system of r equations

$$\sum_{i=1}^{s} x_i a_{ij} = 0, \quad (j = 1, 2, \ldots r) \quad . \qquad . \quad (6.45)$$

with s unknowns has a non-trivial solution, which can be taken as s rational numbers (being ratios of determinants

* See A. C. Aitken, *Determinants and Matrices* (University Mathematical Texts), § 28.

formed from the a_{ij}. Since we may multiply the solution by a fixed number, e.g., by the least common multiple of all the denominators, we may assume that the x_i in (6.45) are in fact integers. We then deduce from (6.44) that

$$\sum_{i=1}^{s} x_i D_i = 0,$$

which contradicts the hypothesis that the D_i form a basis. Therefore we cannot have $s > r$. Similarly $r > s$ is impossible. This proves the invariance of the rank.

We now turn to the general case of a finitely generated Abelian group which possesses elements of finite and of infinite order. Evidently the set of all elements of finite order (including the zero element) form a finite subgroup T, say. Let it be generated by elements $E_1, E_2, \ldots, E_q$ of orders $m_1, m_2, \ldots, m_q$, respectively, where

$$m_i \mid m_{i-1} \ (i = 2, 3, \ldots q).$$

Thus

$$T = \{E_1\} \oplus \{E_2\} \oplus \ldots \oplus \{E_q\}. \qquad . \qquad . \quad (6.46)$$

The difference group $G - T$ is locally infinite, because if a non-zero element $T + X$ (X not in T) were of finite order m we should have

$$m(T + X) \subset T,$$

i.e. $mX \subset T$. Thus mX would be of finite order and hence so would X, which would imply that $X \subset T$, contrary to hypothesis. Also, since G is finitely generated, so is $G - T$.

Applying the preceding theorem to $G - T$, we obtain

$$G - T = \{T + C_1\} \oplus \ldots \oplus \{T + C_r\}. \qquad . \quad (6.47)$$

The significance of the direct sum here is that no element of the form

$$a_1 C_1 + \ldots + a_r C_r$$

can belong to T unless $a_1 = a_2 = \ldots = a_r = 0$.

We can now enunciate the final result.

THEOREM 5. *Let G be a finitely generated Abelian group which contains elements of finite and of infinite order. Then there exist elements E_1, E_2, . . ., E_q of orders m_1, m_2, . . ., m_q respectively, where $m_i \mid m_{i-1}$ ($i = 2, 3, . . ., q$), and elements C_1, C_2, . . ., C_r of infinite order such that*

$$G = \{E_1\} \oplus . . . \oplus \{E_q\} \oplus \{C_1\} \oplus . . . \oplus \{C_r\}. \quad . \quad (6.48)$$

The numbers m_1, m_2, . . ., m_q and r are uniquely determined.

Proof. Let X be an arbitrary element of G. Then $T + X$ is an element of $G - T$ and by (6.47)

$$X = T + x_1 C_1 + . . . + x_r C_r,$$

where T is a certain element of T. Again, by (6.46)

$$T = y_1 E_1 + . . . + y_q E_q,$$

so that

$$X = y_1 E_1 + . . . + y_q E_q + x_1 C_1 + . . . + x_r C_r. \quad (6.49)$$

Suppose now that we have an equation of the form

$$b_1 E_1 + . . . + b_q E_q + a_1 C_1 + . . . + a_r C_r = 0. \quad (6.50)$$

This implies that

$$a_1 C_1 + . . . + a_r C_r$$

is expressible in terms of the E_i and hence that it belongs to T. Therefore $a_1 = . . . = a_r = 0$. Equation (6.50) now reduces to

$$b_1 E_1 + . . . + b_q E_q = 0,$$

which is impossible unless $b_1 = . . . = b_q = 0$ because (6.46) is a direct sum. This proves that (6.48) is a direct sum. The uniqueness of the numbers m_1, m_2, . . ., m_q and r follows from the fact that these are the invariants and the rank of T and $G - T$ respectively.

Example. Find the canonical decomposition for the Abelian group with generators A, B, C, D subject to the relations

$$3A + 9B - 3C = 0, \quad 4A + 2B - 2D = 0. \quad . \quad (6.51)$$

Subtracting the first relation from the second, we obtain the equivalent relations

$$3A + 9B - 3C = 0, \quad A = 7B - 3C + 2D, \quad . \quad (6.52)$$

which shows that the generator A is redundant. Eliminating A, we obtain from the first equation (6.52)

$$6(5B - 2C + D) = 0.$$

Hence if we put

$$U = 5B - 2C + D,$$

the original generators can be expressed in terms of the new set of generators U, B, C, viz.,

$$A = -3B + C + 2U, \quad B = B, \; C = C, \; D = -5B + 2C + U$$

and the relations take the canonical form

$$6U = 0, \; B \text{ and } C \text{ free.}$$

Examples

(1) Prove that if the order of an Abelian group is not divisible by a square, the group must be cyclic.

(2) Show that the greatest invariant (m_1) may be characterized as the maximum order, or alternatively as the least common multiple of all orders in the group.

(3) Show that the residue classes prime to 24 form an Abelian group of order 8 $(= \phi(24))$ and type $(1, 1, 1)$.

(4) Find the elementary divisors and invariants of the following Abelian groups: (i) $15A = 4B = 0$, (ii) $20A = 6B = 5C = 0$, (iii) $12A = 0$, $6A = 15B$.

(5) Prove that in a cyclic group of order g the generating element can be chosen in $\phi(g)$ ways. Deduce from Corollary 2 (p. 146) the well-known formula

$$\phi(g) = g\left(1 - \frac{1}{p}\right)\left(1 - \frac{1}{q}\right)\left(1 - \frac{1}{r}\right). \dots$$

(6) Show that an Abelian group of order g has at least one subgroup whose order is equal to any pre-assigned factor of g.

(7) Prove that every Abelian group is soluble.

(8) Prove that an Abelian group of order p^m and type $(m_1, m_2, \ldots, m_t)$ contains $p^t - 1$ elements of order p.

(9) Show that in an Abelian group of order p^3 and type $(1, 1, 1)$ a basis may be chosen in $p^3(p^3 - 1)(p^2 - 1)(p - 1)$ ways.

(10) Prove that an Abelian group of order p^{2u+v} and type $(2, 2, \ldots, 2, 1, 1, \ldots, 1)$ (u 2's and v 1's) contains

$$p^{u+v-1}(p^u - 1)/(p - 1)$$

cyclic subgroups of order p^2 and

$$(p^{u+v} - 1)(p^{u+v-1} - 1)/(p^2 - 1)(p - 1)$$

non-cyclic subgroups of order p^2.

(11) Find the invariants and rank of the following Abelian groups (i) with generators A, B and relation $2(A + B) = 0$, (ii) with generators A, B, C, D and relations $3A + 5B - 3C = 0$, $4A + 2B - 2D = 0$.

(12) A subgroup of a free Abelian group is free Abelian.

HINTS and ANSWERS. 1. Use Corollary 2, p. 146. 3. No element is of order greater than 2. 4. (i) (4), (3), (5); 60. (ii) (4, 2), (3), (5, 5); 60, 10. (iii) (4), (3, 3), (5); 60, 3. 6. Establish the result first for the case $g = p^m$. 8. The number required is $c_1 - c_0 = c_1 - 1$ and $c_1 = p^t$ by (6.36) and (6.33). 9. By example (8) there are $p^3 - 1$ elements of order p, any one of which can be taken as the first basis element. After the choice has been made, there remain $p^3 - p$ elements from which the second basis element can be selected, etc. 10. (i) There are $p^{2u+v} - p^{u+v}$ elements of order p^2, and in a fixed cyclic group of order p^2 the generating element can be chosen in $p^2 - p$ ways. (ii) Two independent elements of order p can be chosen in $\frac{1}{2}(p^{u+v} - 1)(p^{u+v} - p)$ ways. A fixed group of type $(1, 1)$ has $\frac{1}{2}(p^2 - 1)(p^2 - p)$ alternative sets of generators. 11. (i) $m_1 = 2$, $r = 1$. (ii) $m_1 = 2$, $r = 2$.

CHAPTER VII

GENERATORS AND RELATIONS

46. Finitely Generated and Related Groups. In Chapter IV, p. 44 ff., we discussed a number of groups which were given in terms of generators A, B, ... and certain defining relations, such as $BA = A^{-1}B$. It is evident that every group can be defined in this manner, and this can be done in many ways since it is understood that neither the set of generators nor the set of relations need be irredundant. For example, we may take as generators all the elements of the group and as relations the whole multiplication table. However, in practice it is found that a rather small number of generators and relations suffices to define the group. In order to simplify our discussion we shall confine ourselves to groups which can be defined by a finite number of generators and relations.

On examining more closely this method of defining a group one is led to the study of certain infinite groups, and indeed the method applies whether or not the group is finite.

When we have occasion to refer to theorems of the preceding chapters the reader will have no difficulty in convincing himself that those theorems and their proofs are valid also for infinite groups.

47. Free Groups. We introduce non-commutative symbols X_1, X_2, ..., X_n with which we form **words**, that is formal products

$$W = X_a^{\alpha} X_b^{\beta} \ldots X_r^{\rho} \qquad . \qquad . \qquad . \quad (7.1)$$

consisting of a finite number of factors. The suffixes a, b, ..., r are taken from the set of integers $1, 2, \ldots, n$, repetitions being allowed, since the factors do not commute ; and the exponents α, β, ..., ρ are positive or negative integers. We may regard a word as a function of X_1, X_2, ..., X_n and accordingly write

$$W = w(X_1, X_2, \ldots, X_n).$$

It is convenient to introduce the **empty word**, that is, a word in which the number of factors is zero. The empty word will be denoted by I.

A word is said to be **reduced**, if it is either the empty word or else if it is a product of the form (7.1) in which no two consecutive X's have the same suffix.

Multiplication of two non-empty words U and V is defined as follows : write down the formal product F consisting of the factors U followed by those of V. If F happens to be a reduced word, we define it to be UV. In the contrary case, that is when

$$U = U_0 X^\alpha, \quad V = X^\beta V_0,$$

we simplify F by applying the rule

$$X^\alpha X^\beta = X^{\alpha+\beta}.$$

If $\alpha + \beta = 0$, the factor $X^{\alpha+\beta}$ is removed and further simplifications and cancellations may become possible. The process is continued until a reduced word F_0 is reached. We then define

$$UV = F_0.$$

It should be noted that the process of reduction is well defined so that UV has an unambiguous meaning. The definition of multiplication is supplemented by the obvious rule that

$$UI = IU = U,$$

i.e. the empty word acts as a unit element. The inverse of W is given by

$$W^{-1} = X_r^{-s} \dots X_b^{-\beta} X_a^{-\alpha}.$$

The direct verification of the associative law

$$(PQ)R = P(QR) \qquad . \qquad . \qquad . \qquad (7.2)$$

is somewhat laborious and is best carried out in several stages * which are briefly described as follows :

(i) Let X be a single generator, and let P_0 and R_0 be reduced words (possibly the empty word) such that neither the last factor of P_0 nor the first factor of R_0 is a power of X with non-zero exponent. It is then readily seen that

$$(P_0 X^\alpha)(X^\beta R_0) = P_0(X^{\alpha+\beta} R_0) = (P_0 X^{\alpha+\beta})R_0 \qquad (7.3)$$

In this relation the exponents may be any integers including zero, if we use the convention that

$$X^0 = I.$$

(ii) If P and R are any reduced words and X is any generator, then

$$(PX^\alpha)R = P(X^\alpha R) ; \qquad . \qquad . \qquad . \qquad (7.4)$$

for we may write

$$P = P_0 X^\pi, \quad R = X^\phi R_0,$$

where P_0 and R_0 are as in (i) and π and ϕ are integers. We then have

$$(PX^\alpha)R = ((P_0 X^\pi)X^\alpha)(X^\phi R_0) = (P_0 X^{\pi+\alpha})(X^\phi R_0)$$
$$= P_0(X^{\pi+\alpha+\phi} R_0)$$
$$= P_0(X^\pi(X^{\alpha+\phi} R_0)) = P_0(X^\pi(X^\alpha R))$$
$$= (P_0 X^\pi)(X^\alpha R)$$
$$= P(X^\alpha R).$$

(iii) Finally, in order to prove (7.2) in general, we argue by induction on the number of factors in Q. The case in

* See A. G. Kurosh, *The theory of groups*, vol. 1, p. 126.

which Q reduces to a single factor X^α is covered by (7.2). Assume now that

$$Q = Q_0 X^\alpha$$

and that the associative law holds with Q_0 in place of Q. We then have

$$(PQ)R = (P(Q_0 X^\alpha))R = ((PQ_0)X^\alpha)R = (PQ_0)(X^\alpha R)$$
$$= P(Q_0(X^\alpha R))$$

$$= P((Q_0 X^\alpha)R) = P(QR).$$

This completes the verification of (7.2) in all cases.

The set of reduced words in the symbols $X_1, X_2, \ldots, X_n$ with the law of composition just defined forms an infinite group ; it is called the **free group** generated by

$$X_1, X_2, \ldots, X_n.$$

The free group on a single generator, X, is the infinite cyclic group X ; it consists of the elements

$$I(=X^0), X, X^{-1}, X^2, X^{-2}, \ldots$$

and is isomorphic with the additive group of integers (see § 3, (ii)).

For example, in the case of two generators X and Y, typical products are

$$(XY^{-2}X)(YX) = XY^{-2}XYX$$

$$(XY^2)(Y^{-1}X) = XYX$$

$$(XYX^{-1})(XY^{-1}X) = X^2.$$

To summarize we may say that the free group on $X_1, X_2, \ldots, X_n$ consists of all reduced words in these symbols and that these are subject only to the trivial conditions

$$X_i X_i^{-1} = X_i^{-1}X_i = I \ (i = 1, 2, \ldots, n)$$

and their consequences.

48. Relations. Let G be a given group which is generated by n of its elements, say

$$G = \{G_1,\, G_2,\, \ldots,\, G_n\} \quad .$$

Then every element of G is a product of the form

$$G = G_a{}^\alpha\, G_b{}^\beta \, \ldots \, G_r{}^\rho \qquad . \qquad . \qquad . \quad (7.5)$$

(see p. 42). If G is not a free group, there are non-trivial equalities such as

$$G_a{}^\alpha\, G_b{}^\beta \, \ldots \, G_r{}^\rho = G_{a'}{}^{\alpha'} G_{b'}{}^{\beta'} \, \ldots \, G_{r'}{}^{\rho'} \; ;$$

a relation like this can clearly be written

$$r(G_1,\, G_2,\, \ldots,\, G_n) = I. \qquad . \qquad . \qquad . \quad (7.6)$$

In order to analyze the situation in more detail we consider the free group F on n symbols $X_1,\, X_2,\, \ldots,\, X_n$ and define a mapping θ of F on to G by the rule that

$$\theta(w(X_1,\, X_2,\, \ldots,\, X_n)) = w(G_1 G_2\,,\ldots,\, G_n) \quad . \quad (7.7)$$

that is, the image under θ of any product of the X's is the corresponding product of the G's. The important fact to note is that θ is a homomorphism of F on to G. Thus if W_1 and W_2 are elements of F, then

$$\theta(W_1 W_2) = \theta(W_1)\ \theta(W_2) \; ; \qquad . \qquad . \quad (7.8)$$

for $W_1 W_2$ is defined as the reduced word obtained by juxtaposition of W_1 and W_2 and subsequent simplification, as described in the preceding section. The application of θ consists in replacing each X by the corresponding G. Since the same simplifications can be carried out with the G's, it follows that the multiplication defined for free groups is valid in any group whatever, which is all that (7.8) means. Since θ is now known to be a homomorphic mapping, it may more simply be defined by

$$\theta(X_i) = G_i \quad (i = 1,\, 2,\, \ldots,\, n), \qquad . \qquad . \quad (7.9)$$

from which (7.8) follows by repeated application.

Let the kernel of θ be R. As we have seen in § 34, this is a certain invariant subgroup of F; it consists of all those elements $r(X_1, X_2, \ldots, X_n)$ of F for which

$$r(G_1, G_2, \ldots, G_n) = I ; \qquad . \qquad . \qquad (7.10)$$

or to put it differently, R consists of exactly those words

$$R = r(X_1, X_2, \ldots, X_n) \qquad . \qquad . \qquad (7.11)$$

which become left-hand sides of relations in G when X_i is replaced by G_i. We shall say that the element R of F corresponds to the relation (7.6) in G.

We recall also that

$$G = F/R . \qquad . \qquad . \qquad . \qquad (7.12)$$

Summarizing our results, we can state the following theorem :

THEOREM 1. *Every group G which can be generated by n elements can be represented as a homomorphic image of the free group F on n generators. The kernel of the homomorphic mapping of F on to G consists of those elements of F which correspond to relations in G.*

The groups F and R which occur in (7.12) are said to form a **presentation** of G. A group may have many such presentations.

Conversely, we may start with any invariant subgroup R of the free group F on $X_1, X_2, \ldots, X_n$ and then form G/R. This group has generators $X_i R$ $(i = 1, 2, \ldots, n)$ and relations $r(G_1, G_2, \ldots, G_n) = I$, where $r(X_1, X_2, \ldots, X_n)$ ranges over R; for $q(G_1, G_2, \ldots, G_n) = I$ is a relation for G if and only if $q(X_1, X_2, \ldots, X_n)R = R$, i.e.

$$q(X_1, X_2, \ldots, X_n) \subset R.$$

49. Definition of Groups. We shall now discuss in more detail what is meant by saying that a group is defined by n generators

$$G_1, G_2, \ldots, G_n \qquad . \qquad . \qquad . \qquad (7.13)$$

M

and m relations

$$r_k(G_1, G_2, \ldots, G_n) = I \quad (k = 1, 2, \ldots, m) \quad . \quad (7.14)$$

The first question that arises concerns the existence of such a group. In a sense, the answer is trivial; for since it is not required that the generators or the relations should be irredundant, it is obvious that the trivial group, for which

$$G_1 = G_2 = \ldots = G_n = I,$$

satisfies any set of relations. More generally, if **G** satisfies (7.14), so does any homomorph **H** of **G**, the generators of **H** being the images of **G**. What we really seek is the " largest " or " freest " group satisfying (7.14). To make the meaning of this statement more precise we consider the free group **F** on $X_1, X_2, \ldots, X_n$. With the relations (7.14) we associate the elements

$$R_k = r_k(X_1, X_2, \ldots, X_n) \quad (k = 1, 2, \ldots, m) \quad (7.15)$$

of **F**. Evidently we may assume these to be reduced words and therefore legitimate elements of **F**. Now it is clear that from the given relations we may derive further relations for **G** ; in fact, if $r_j(G_1, \ldots, G_n) = I$ and $r_k(G_1, \ldots, G_n) = I$ are relations, so are

$$r_j(G_1, \ldots, G_n)\, r_k(G_1, \ldots, G_n) = I,$$

$$\{r_j(G_1, \ldots, G_n)\}^{-1} = I, \quad G^{-1}\{r_j(G_1, \ldots, G_n)\}G = I,$$

where G is any element of **G**. Thus in terms of the group **F**, we may say that each element of the least normal subgroup of **F** containing $R_1, R_2, \ldots, R_m$ corresponds to a relation in **G**. This group will be denoted by

$$R = \{R_1, R_2, \ldots, R_m\}^F \quad . \quad . \quad . \quad (7.16)$$

and is called the **normal closure** of $R_1, R_2, \ldots, R_m$. It may briefly be described as the **relation group** of **G**. It consists of the minimal set of those elements of **F** which correspond to the relations (7.14) or their consequences.

Next, consider a group H on n generators $H_1, H_2, \ldots, H_n$ which satisfy the same relations as the generators of G, viz.

$$r_i(H_1, H_2, \ldots, H_n) = I \quad (i = 1, 2, \ldots, m) \quad . \quad (7.17)$$

and some additional relations

$$t_j(H_1, H_2, \ldots, H_n) = I \quad (j = 1, 2, \ldots, p) \quad . \quad (7.18)$$

and suppose that (7.17) and (7.18) together constitute a complete set of defining relations for H. Let

$$T_j = t_j(X_1, X_2, \ldots, X_n) \quad (j = 1, 2, \ldots, p)$$

be the elements of F that correspond to (7.18). Then

$$S = \{R_1, \ldots, R_m, T_1, \ldots, T_p\}^F$$

is the relation group of H and

$$H = F/S.$$

Since $S \supset R$ we may, as in the Second Isomorphism Theorem (p. 112), regard $A = S/R$ as an invariant subgroup of $F/R (= G)$. It then follows that $H \cong G/A$. Thus we have the result :

THEOREM 2. *If new relations are added to those satisfied by a group G, the resulting group is a homomorphic image of G.* We can now state that the group F/R is the freest group with n generators and relations (7.14), where R is defined in (7.16). This answers the question raised at the beginning of this section.

As an application of these ideas we mention the process of *making a group G Abelian*, that is, of passing from G to G/G', which is its largest Abelian homomorph. This amounts to adding the relations

$$G_i^{-1} G_j^{-1} G_i G_j = I \quad (i < j ; \; i, j = 1, 2, \ldots, n)$$

to the existing relations. The structure of G/G' may then be found directly by the methods of Chapter VI.

Example. Find the structure of G/G' when G is the quaternion group

$$A^4 = I, \quad A^2 = B^2, \quad BA = A^3 B$$

(see p. 52). The group G/G' is generated by the cosets $U = AG'$, $V = BG'$. Using the additive notation, we obtain the relations

$$4U = 0, \quad 2U = 2V, \quad V + U = 3U + V,$$

which reduce to

$$2U = 2V = 0.$$

Hence G/G' is the Abelian group of type $(2, 2)$.

If the free group on $X_1, X_2, \ldots, X_n$ is made Abelian in this way, we obtain the free Abelian group on these generators (see p. 152). From this remark it follows incidentally that free groups on different numbers of generators cannot be isomorphic. For let F_m and F_n be free groups on m and n generators respectively and suppose they are isomorphic. Then F_m/F_m' and F_n/F_n' would also be isomorphic; but these are free Abelian groups on m and n generators respectively and by Theorem 4 of § 45 cannot be isomorphic unless $m = n$.

Finally, we mention without proof* the important theorem that every subgroup of a free group which contains more than one element is itself a free group.

For a proof see Kurosh, *loc. cit.* vol. 2, p. 28.

Examples

(1) Show that the derived group of a free group on n generators consists of those elements in which the sum of the exponents for each generator is equal to zero. (E.g. $X_1 X_2^{-1} X_1^{-2} X_2 X_1$.)

(2) Find the structure of G/G' when G is one or the other of the groups of order 12 described in ex. (7) on p. 61.

(3) Let R be an invariant subgroup of F and let $[F, R]$ be the group generated by all elements of the form $f^{-1} r^{-1} f r$, where f ranges over F and r over R. Prove that $[F, R]$ is invariant in F and that $R/[F, R]$ is in the centre of $F/[F, R]$.

ANSWERS.   (2) (i) $(2, 2)$; (ii) (4).

BIBLIOGRAPHY

BURNSIDE, WM., *Theory of groups of finite order*, 2nd ed., 1911. (Reprint by Dover Publications, Inc., 1955.)

CARMICHAEL, R. D., *Introduction to the theory of groups of finite order*, 1937.

HILTON, H., *An Introduction to the theory of groups of finite order*, 1908.

KUROSH, A. G., *The theory of groups*, 2 vols. (transl. from the Russian by K. A. Hirsch), New York, 1955.

MATHEWSON, L. C., *Elementary theory of groups*, 1930.

MILLER, G. A., BLICHFELD, H. F., DICKSON, L. E., *Theory and applications of finite groups*, 1916.

SPEISER, A., *Theorie der Gruppen von endlicher Ordnung*, 3rd ed., 1937 (American reprint 1945).

ZASSENHAUS, H., *The theory of groups* (transl. from the German by S. Kraivety), New York, 1949.

INDEX

The numbers refer to the pages

169